ENZYMATIC
SYNTHESIS OF DNA

CIBA LECTURES IN MICROBIAL BIOCHEMISTRY

1956 H. A. Barker, *Bacterial Fermentations*

1957 E. P. Abraham, *Biochemistry of Some Peptide and Steroid Antibiotics*

1959 E. F. Gale, *Synthesis and Organisation in the Bacterial Cell*

1960 M. R. J. Salton, *Microbial Cell Walls*

1961 A. Kornberg, *Enzymatic Synthesis of DNA*

CIBA   LECTURES IN MICROBIAL BIOCHEMISTRY

ENZYMATIC SYNTHESIS OF DNA

BY ARTHUR KORNBERG

1961

JOHN WILEY & SONS, INC.

New York · London · Sydney

The CIBA Lectures in Microbial Biochemistry were established in 1955 at the Institute of Microbiology, Rutgers, The State University of New Jersey, through the support of CIBA Pharmaceutical Products Inc., Summit, N. J. The lectures are given in the spring of each year at the Institute of Microbiology, New Brunswick, N. J.

THIRD PRINTING, APRIL, 1965

Copyright © 1962 by John Wiley & Sons, Inc.

All rights reserved
This book or any part thereof must not be reproduced in any form without the written permission of the publisher.

Library of Congress Catalog Card Number: 62-20165
Printed in the United States of America

PREFACE

When enzymes in the test tube catalyze a reaction sequence of unimagined complexity, it is one of the happiest accidents in biochemistry. The biochemist stutters a description and then joins a rush of investigators to unravel it. These three chapters, presented as lectures, record our early and more recent encounters with the enzymatic synthesis of DNA. I am grateful to have had the companionship of I. R. Lehman, M. J. Bessman, my wife Sylvy, and E. S. Simms early in this work. J. Adler, J. Josse, S. B. Zimmerman, H. K. Schachman, C. M. Radding, H. V. Aposhian, A. D. Kaiser, M. N. Swartz, and T. A. Trautner have participated since then in our attempts to understand DNA biosynthesis.

I acknowledge with pleasure the hospitality of J. O. Lampen and the Institute of Microbiology at Rutgers and the generosity of S. Barkulis and CIBA Pharmaceutical Products Inc., who made this lecture series and publication possible.

ARTHUR KORNBERG

Department of Biochemistry
Stanford University School of Medicine
Palo Alto, California
August 1962

CONTENTS

chapter 1   Replication of DNA 1

    Structure of DNA
    Enzymatic Approach to Replication
    Properties of the Enzyme: Polymerase
    Evidence for Base-Pairing Mechanism of
      Replication
        Physical Properties of Enzymatically Synthesized DNA
        Substitution of Analogs
        Chemical Composition
        Enzymatic Replication of Nucleotide Sequences
            Replication of the Nucleotide Composition
            Base Pairing and Opposite Polarity of Strands
            Nonrandomness of Nearest-Neighbor Frequencies

Nearest-Neighbor Sequence Frequencies in Native and Enzymatically Produced DNA; in *Bacillus subtilis* DNA
Replication of Single-Stranded DNA
Requirement for Four Triphosphates and DNA for DNA Synthesis
Some Unsolved Questions
Summary and Conclusions
References

chapter 2 De Novo Synthesis of DNA-Like Polymers   38

dAT Copolymer
    Time Course of Unprimed (De Novo) Synthesis
    Priming Activity of Product of De Novo Synthesis
    Characterization of dAT Copolymer
    Size of Polymer during De Novo Synthesis
    Kinetics of De Novo and Primed Synthesis
    Sensitive Detection of De Novo Polymer Synthesis during the "Lag" Phase
dGdC Polymer
    De Novo and Primed Synthesis
    Characterization of dGdC Polymer
    Mechanism of De Novo and Primed Synthesis
    Analogs of the dAT and dGdC Polymers and Their Uses
    Formation of Hybrid Molecules from Two Polymers
    Does a dAT Copolymer Occur Naturally?
Summary and Conclusions
References

chapter 3 DNA Synthesis in Bacteriophage-Infected Cells   69

Synthesis of HMC Deoxynucleoside Monophosphate
Synthesis of HMC Deoxynucleoside Triphosphate

Exclusion of Cytosine from Incorporation into DNA
  Synthesis of Glucosylated HMC Residues in DNA
    Glucosylation in T2 Infection
    Glucosylation in T4 Infection
    Glucosylation in T6 Infection
  DNA Polymerase
Summary and Conclusions
References

CHAPTER

1

REPLICATION OF DNA

We need not review the recent discoveries [1-3] that identify deoxyribonucleic (DNA) as the genetic substance. In its role DNA must have two functions: it must contain information, in chemical code, to direct the development of the cell according to its inheritance, and it must be reproducible in exact replica for the transmission of this inheritance to future generations.

Are these two functions, the expression of the code (protein synthesis) and the copying of the code (preservation of the race), inextricably integrated or can they be studied separately? Encouraging studies are current in several laboratories on DNA-directed synthesis of a "messenger RNA" which may prove to direct protein synthesis.[4] What we have learned from our studies over the last several years is that the replication of DNA distinct from protein synthesis can be examined and at least partially understood at the enzymatic level.

Structure of DNA

First we shall review very briefly some aspects of DNA structure that are essential for this discussion. Analysis of samples of DNA from a variety of sources, by many investigators,[5] has revealed the remarkable fact that the purine content always equals the pyrimidine content. Among the purines, the adenine content may differ considerably from the guanine, and among the pyrimidines, the thymine from the cytosine. However, there is an equivalence of the bases with an amino group in the 6-position of the ring to the bases with a keto group in the 6-position. Watson and Crick,[6] in their masterful hypothesis of the structure of DNA, proposed that the 6-amino group of adenine is linked by hydrogen bonds to the 6-keto group of thymine and that guanine is hydrogen-bonded to cytosine, thus accounting for the equivalence of the purines to the pyrimidines (Fig. 1).

On the basis of models, X-ray crystallographic measurements by Wilkins et al.,[7] and chemical data, Watson and Crick proposed a structure for DNA in which two polynucleotide strands are wound about each other in a helical manner. Figure 2 is a diagram of a fragment of a DNA chain about 10 nucleotide units long. According to physical measurements, DNA chains are 10,000 or more units long. We see here the deoxypentose rings linked by phosphate residues to form the backbone of the chain; the purine and pyrimidine rings are the planar structures emerging at right angles from the main axis of the chain. Figure 3 is a space-filling molecular model [8] and gives a better idea of the packing of the atoms in the structure. The purine and pyrimidine bases of one chain are bonded to the pyrimidine and purine bases of the complementary chain by the hydrogen bonds described in Fig. 1. Extension of

Fig. 1.

Hydrogen bonding of adenine to thymine

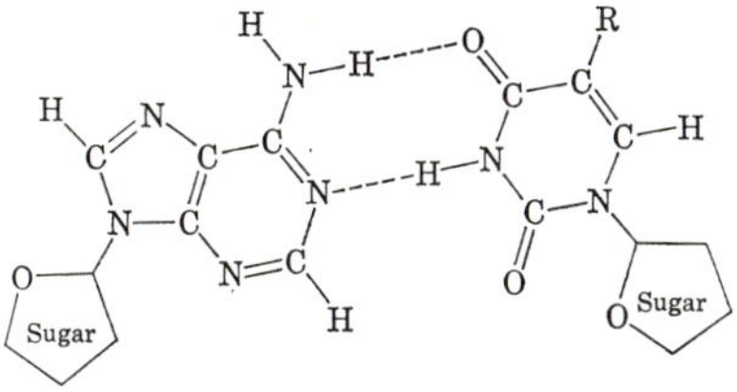

R	
—CH₃	Thymine
—H	Uracil
—Br	Bromouracil
—F	Fluorouracil

Hydrogen bonding of guanine to cytosine

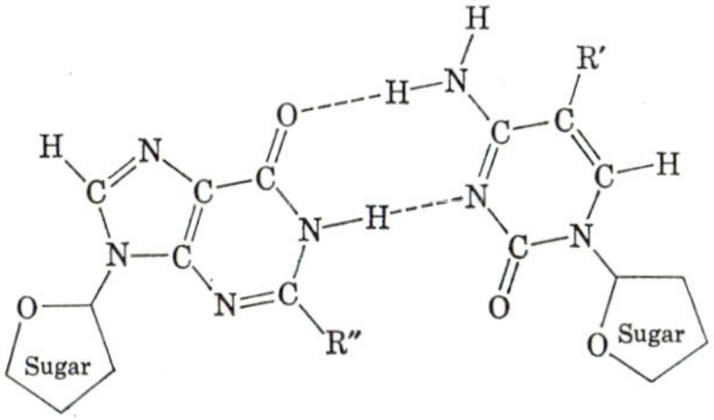

R'		R''	
—H	Cytosine	—NH₂	Guanine
—CH₃	Methylcytosine	—H	Hypoxanthine
—Br	Bromocytosine	=O	Xanthine
—F	Fluorocytosine		

a molecular model (manually) in Fig. 4 shows more clearly how the hydrogen-bonded base pairs are stacked in the double-helical structure.

The X-ray measurements have indicated that the space between the opposing chains in the model agrees with the calculated value for the hydrogen-bond linkage of a purine to a pyrimidine; it is too small for two purines and too large for two pyrimidines. Most rewarding from the biological point of view, the structure provides a useful model

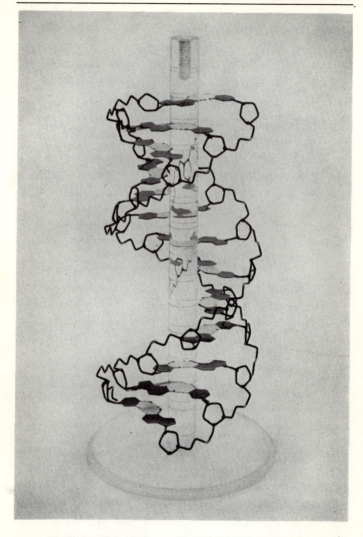

Fig. 2. Double helical structure of DNA. (Watson and Crick model.)

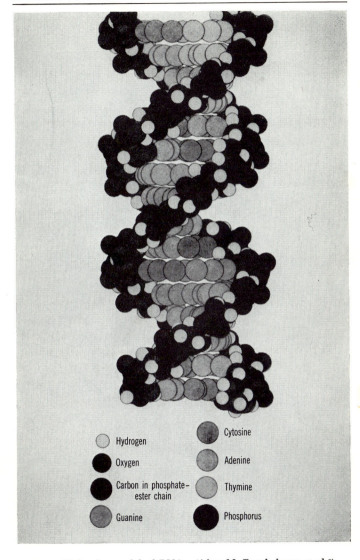

Fig. 3. Molecular model of DNA. (After M. Feughelman et al.[8])

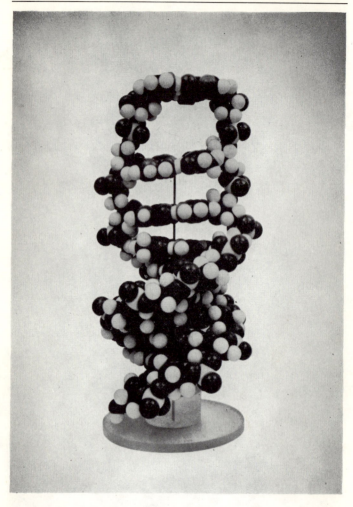

Fig. 4. Extended molecular model of DNA. (Courtesy of Dr. Alan Hodge.)

to explain how cellular replication of DNA may come about. For, if you imagine that these two chains separate and that a new chain is formed complementary to each of them, the result will be two pairs of strands, each pair identical to the original parent duplex (see Fig. 10).

Enzymatic Approach to Replication

Now that we have in the Watson and Crick proposal a mechanical model of replication, we may pose the question: What is the chemical mechanism by which this super molecule is built up in the cell? Observations by Meselson and Stahl [9] with dividing *Escherichia coli*, by Taylor [10] with growing bean plants, and by Sueoka [11] with the alga *Chlamydomonas* are all consistent with and lend support to the Watson and Crick replication model. However, these experiments with intact cells cannot by themselves provide the definitive proof for the precise chemical events, as illustrated by Cavalieri's recent objections.[12] Studies with broken-cell systems must therefore be pursued to try to elucidate the chemical reactions involved in DNA replication. Some 60 years ago the alcoholic fermentation of sugar by a yeast cell was considered to be a process inseparable from the living cell, but through the Büchner discovery of fermentation in extracts and the progress of enzymology during the first half of this century we understand fermentation by yeast as a sequence of integrated chemical reactions. The synthesis of DNA was also regarded for a long time in a "vitalistic" fashion: tampering with the genetic apparatus could produce nothing but disorder. This prediction was not warranted, nor should a similar pessimism govern our attitude toward the many unsolved problems of cellular structure and specialized function.

For an effective approach to the problem of nucleic-acid biosynthesis it is essential to understand the biosynthesis of the simple nucleotides and the coenzymes and to have these concepts and methodologies well in hand. It was from these studies that we developed the conviction that an activated nucleoside 5′-phosphate is the basic biosynthetic building block of the nucleic acids.[13] It will be recalled that the main pathways of purine and pyrimidine biosynthesis all lead to the nucleoside 5′-phosphate;[13] they do not usually include the free bases or nucleosides, except as salvage mechanisms. Although the 2′- and 3′-isomers of the nucleotides are known, they probably arise mainly from certain types of enzymatic degradation of the nucleic acids. It will also be recalled from the biosynthesis of coenzymes,[14] the simplest of the nucleotide condensation products, that it is adenosine triphosphate (ATP) that condenses with nicotinamide mononucleotide to form diphosphopyridine nucleotide, with riboflavin phosphate to form flavine adenine dinucleotide (FAD), with pantetheine phosphate to form the precursor of coenzyme A, and so forth. Uridine, cytidine, and guanosine coenzymes are likewise formed from the respective triphosphates of the nucleosides. The

$$\text{Adenosine—O—P(=O)(O}^-\text{):O—P(=O)(O}^-\text{)—O—P(=O)(O}^-\text{)—O}^-$$

$$\text{Nucleoside—O—\overset{..}{P}(=O)—O}^-$$

Fig. 5. Nucleophilic attack of a nucleoside monophosphate on ATP.

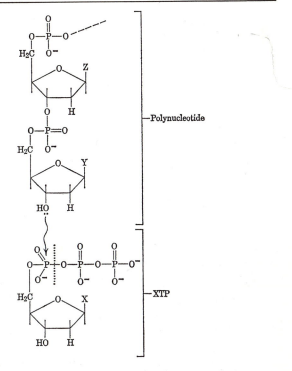

Fig. 6. Postulated mechanism for extending a DNA chain.

activation of fatty acids and amino acids is an example of the same pattern of reaction mechanism.

This mechanism (Fig. 5), in which a nucleophilic attack [15] on the pyrophosphoryl-activated adenyl group by a nucleoside monophosphate leads to the formation of a coenzyme, was adopted as a working hypothesis for studying the synthesis of a DNA chain. As illustrated in Fig. 6, it was postulated that the basic building block is a deoxynucleoside 5′-triphosphate which is attacked by the 3′-hydroxyl group at the growing end of a polydeoxynucleotide chain; inorganic pyrophosphate is eliminated, and the chain is lengthened by one unit. The results of our studies of DNA synthesis, as shown below, are in keeping with this type of reaction.

Properties of the Enzyme: Polymerase

First let us consider the enzyme and comment on its discovery.[13,16] Mixing the triphosphates of the four deoxynucleosides which commonly occur in DNA with an extract of thymus, bone marrow, or *E. coli* would not be expected to lead to the net synthesis of DNA. Instead, as might be expected, the destruction of DNA by the extracts of such cells and tissues was by far the predominant process, and one had to resort to isotopic tracer methods to detect such a biosynthetic reaction. We used C^{14}-labeled substrate of high specific radioactivity and incubated it with ATP and extracts of *E. coli*, an organism that reproduces itself every 20 minutes. The first positive results represented the conversion of only a very small fraction of the acid-soluble substrate into an acid-insoluble fraction (50 or so counts out of a million added). Although this was only a few micromicromoles of reaction, it was something. Through this crack we tried to drive a wedge, and the hammer was enzyme purification.[17]

This has been and still is a major preoccupation. Our best preparations are several thousandfold enriched with respect to protein over the crude extracts, but still present are one or more of the several varieties of nuclease and diesterase activities that occur in the *E. coli* cell. The occurrence of what appears to be a similar DNA-synthesizing system in animal cells as well as in other bacterial species has been observed.[18] We must wait for more exten-

$$n \text{ dTPPP} + n \text{ dGPPP} + n \text{ dAPPP} + n \text{ dCPPP} + \text{DNA} \rightleftharpoons \text{DNA} - \begin{bmatrix} \text{dTP} \\ \text{dGP} \\ \text{dAP} \\ \text{dCP} \end{bmatrix}_n + 4(n)\text{PP}$$

Fig. 7. Equation for enzymatic synthesis of DNA.

sive purification of the enzymes from these sources in order to make valid comparisons with the *E. coli* system.

The requirements for net synthesis of DNA with the purified *E. coli* enzyme [19] are shown in the equation in Fig. 7. All four of the deoxynucleotides which form the adenine-thymine and guanine-cytosine couples must be present. The substrates must be the tri- and not the di-phosphates, and only the deoxy sugar compounds are active. DNA must be present; DNA from animal, plant, bacterial, or viral sources serves equally well in the synthesis, provided the molecular weight is high. The product of the synthesis, which is discussed further below, accumulates until one of the substrates is exhausted and may be 20 or more times greater in amount than the DNA added; thus it is derived to the extent of 95% or more from the substrates added to the reaction mixture. Inorganic pyrophosphate is released in quantities equimolar to the deoxynucleotides converted to DNA.

If one of these substrates were omitted, the extent of the reaction would be diminished by a factor of more than 100. It turns out that when one of the deoxynucleotide substrates is lacking, an extremely small yet significant quantity of nucleotide is linked to the DNA primer. My co-workers and I have described this so-called "limited reaction"[20] and have shown that under these circumstances a few deoxynucleotides are added to the nucleoside ends of some of the DNA chains but that further synthesis is blocked for lack of the missing nucleotides. Current studies show that this limited reaction is governed, as is extensive synthesis, by the hydrogen-bonding of adenine to thymine and of guanine to cytosine.

When all four triphosphates are present, but when DNA is omitted, no reaction takes place at all. What is the basis for this requirement? Does the DNA function as a primer in the manner of glycogen in the phosphorylase reaction, or does it function as a template directing the synthesis of

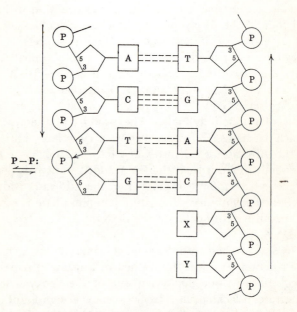

Fig. 8. Mechanism for enzymatic DNA replication.

exact copies of itself? We have good reason to believe that it is the latter, and as the central and restricted theme of this book, I should like to emphasize that it is the capacity for base pairing by hydrogen bonding between the pre-existing DNA and the nucleotides added as substrates that accounts for the requirement for DNA.

The enzyme we are studying is thus unique in present experience in that it takes directions from a template—it matches the particular purine or pyrimidine substrate which will form a hydrogen-bonded pair with a base on the template (Fig. 8). Six major lines of evidence that support this thesis are cited.

Evidence for Base-Pairing Mechanism of Replication

Physical Properties of Enzymatically Synthesized DNA. From collaborative studies with Howard K. Schachman, to whom we are greatly indebted, it can be said that the enzymatic product is indistinguishable from high-molecular-weight, double-stranded DNA isolated from natural sources.[21] (It might be mentioned again that in these descriptions, as in those of the chemical nature of DNA, discussed below, 90 to 95% of the DNA sample comes from the deoxynucleoside triphosphate substrates.) The synthesized product has a sedimentation coefficient in the neighborhood of 25 and reduced viscosity of 40 dl/g and on the basis of these measurements we believe it to be a long, stiff rod with a molecular weight of about six million. When the synthesized DNA is heated, the rod collapses and the molecule becomes a compact, randomly coiled structure; it may be inferred that the hydrogen bonds holding the strands together have melted, and this is borne out by characteristic changes in the viscometric and optical properties of the molecule.* Similar results are found upon cleavage of the molecule by pancreatic deoxyribonuclease. In all these respects the enzymatically synthesized DNA is indistinguishable from the material isolated from natural sources and may thus be presumed to have a hydrogen-bonded structure similar to natural DNA.

Would one imagine that the collapsed, jumbled strands of heated DNA would serve as a primer for DNA synthesis? Very likely not. Picturing a jumbled strand of twine, one might regard collapsed DNA as a hopeless template for replication. Nevertheless, the collapsed structure is an excellent primer, and the nonviscous, randomly coiled, single-stranded DNA leads to the synthesis of highly viscous, double-stranded DNA.[22] Sinsheimer has isolated from the tiny ϕX174 virus a DNA which appears to be single-stranded.[23] Like heated DNA, it has proved to be an excellent primer [22] and a useful material in studies [24] that demonstrate in density-gradient sedimentations its progressive conversion to a double-stranded condition during the course of enzymatic synthesis.

Although a detailed discussion of the physical aspects of replication is not feasible in this book, it should be mentioned that the DNA in the single-stranded condition is not only a suitable primer but is the preferred form with certain of the enzyme preparations. With such preparations of the *E. coli* enzyme, and even more strikingly with a polymerase induced by infection of *E. coli* [25] with bacteriophage T2, the native, double-stranded DNA is relatively inert unless it is modified. Bollum has made similar observations

---

* DNA isolated from nature fails to recover its original optical density and melting behavior when cooled rapidly after melting. This hysteresis effect has not been seen with several samples of enzymatically synthesized DNA (unpublished observations of S. B. Zimmerman and A. Kornberg).

on a requirement for heated DNA by the enzyme that he has purified from calf thymus.[26]

Substitution of Analogs. From the many interesting reports on the incorporation of bromouracil,[27] azaguanine,[28] and other analogs into bacterial and viral DNA, it might be surmised that some latitude in the structure of the bases can be tolerated, provided there is no interference with the hydrogen bonding. Deoxyuridine triphosphate or 5-bromodeoxyuridine triphosphate were found to be utilized for enzymatic DNA synthesis when substituted for deoxythymidine triphosphate but not for deoxyadenosine, deoxyguanosine, or deoxycytidine triphosphates; 5-methyl- and 5-bromocytosine specifically replaced cytosine; hypoxanthine substituted only for guanine (Table 1).[29] These and the more recent findings with 5-fluoropyrimidine nucleotides are best interpreted on the basis of hydrogen bonding of the adenine-thymine and guanine-cytosine type (Fig. 1, Table 1).

Along these lines it is relevant to mention the existence of a naturally occurring "analog" of cytosine, hydroxymethylcytosine (HMC), which is found in place of cytosine in the DNA of the *E. coli* bacteriophages of the T-even series [30] and is considered in detail in Chapter 3. In this case the DNA contains equivalent amounts of HMC and guanine and equivalent amounts of adenine and thymine. The DNA's of T2, T4, and T6 bacteriophages contain glucose linked to the hydroxymethyl groups of the HMC in ratios characteristic for each phage,[31, 32] and in T2 and T6 some of the HMC groups contain no glucose.[32] These characteristics have posed problems regarding the synthesis of these DNA's that might appear to be incompatible with the simple base-pairing hypothesis. Exploration of this problem, as described in Chapter 3, has revealed that the reaction of the polymerase from virus-infected cells is indeed governed by the usual hydrogen-bonding restrictions.

TABLE 1

Replacement of Natural Bases by Analogs in Enzymatic Synthesis of DNA

Analog, Used in Form of Deoxynucleoside Triphosphate	Deoxynucleoside Triphosphate Replaced by Analog			
	dTTP	dATP	dCTP	dGTP
	% of Control Value			
Uracil	54	0	0	0
5-Bromouracil	97(100)	0(0)	0(0)	0(0)
5-Fluorouracil *	32(9)	0(0)	0(0)	0(0)
5-Hydroxymethylcytosine	(0)	(0)	(98)	(0)
5-Methylcytosine	0	0	185	0
5-Bromocytosine	0(0)	0(0)	118(104)	0(0)
5-Fluorocytosine †	0(0)	0(0)	63(67)	0(0)
N-methyl-5-fluorocytosine	0	0	0	0
Hypoxanthine	0	0	0	25
Xanthine	0	0	0	0

Values in parentheses were measured with T2 polymerase (see Chapter 3); the others were measured with *E. coli* polymerase. Zero values represent those of less than 2% in most cases and in all cases do not differ significantly from the background of this assay. Control values were measured as rates of radioactive deoxynucleotide incorporation into DNA in a standard assay system in the presence of dTTP, dATP, dCTP, and dGTP, with heated salmon sperm DNA as primer for T2 polymerase and calf thymus DNA for *E. coli* polymerase.

* Gift of Dr. C. Heidelberger.
† Gift of Dr. R. Duschinsky.

Chemical Composition.

We may ask two questions. First, has the enzymatic product the equivalence of adenine to thymine and of guanine to cytosine that characterize natural DNA? Second, does the composition of the natural DNA used as primer determine the composition of the product?

In Table 2 are the results that answer these two questions.[33,35] The experiments are identical, except that in each case a different DNA primer was used. In the enzymatically synthesized DNA the adenine content equals the thymine and the guanine equals the cytosine; thus the purine content is in every case identical to the pyrimidine. The characteristic ratio of adenine-thymine pairs to guanine-cytosine pairs of a given DNA primer is imposed rather faithfully on the product that is synthesized. Whether the net DNA increase is only 1% or 1000%, the results are the same. It has not been possible either to distort these base ratios by using widely differing molar concentrations of substrates.

In the last line of Table 2 is a novel "DNA," dAT copolymer [34] (see Chapter 2). Suffice it to say at this point that it is a copolymer of deoxyadenylate and deoxythymidylate that has the physical size and properties of natural DNA and in which the adenine and thymine are in a perfectly alternating sequence. When this DNA-like polymer is used as a primer, new dAT polymer synthesis starts immediately, and even though all four triphosphates are present no trace of guanine or cytosine can be detected in the product. The conclusion thus seems inescapable that the base composition is replicated in the enzymatic synthesis and that hydrogen-bonding of adenine to thymine and of guanine to cytosine is the guiding mechanism.

Enzymatic Replication of Nucleotide Sequences.

The genetic code in DNA is considered to be spelled out by a

TABLE 2

Nucleotide Composition of Enzymatically Synthesized DNA

Primer DNA	Ap	Tp	Gp	Cp	$\frac{Ap+Gp}{Tp+Cp}$	$\frac{Ap+Tp}{Gp+Cp}$	Chemical Analysis of Primer $\frac{A+T}{G+C}$
Micrococcus lysodeikticus	0.147	0.145	0.354	0.354	1.00	0.41	0.39
Mycobacterium phlei	0.164	0.162	0.337	0.337	1.00	0.48	0.49
Aerobacter aerogenes	0.220	0.223	0.280	0.277	1.00	0.80	0.82
Escherichia coli	0.248	0.254	0.249	0.249	0.99	1.01	0.97
Bacteriophages λ and λ dg	0.247	0.252	0.249	0.252	0.99	1.00	1.06
Bacillus subtilis	0.278	0.280	0.222	0.220	1.00	1.26	1.29
Calf thymus	0.286	0.283	0.214	0.217	1.00	1.32	1.25
Hemophilus influenzae	0.310	0.308	0.191	0.191	1.00	1.62	1.64
Bacteriophages T2, T4 and T6	0.319	0.318	0.188	0.179	1.01	1.76	1.84
dAT copolymer	0.500	0.500	<0.002	<0.002	1.00	>250	>40

The values in the first four columns are taken from the nucleotide sums of the nearest neighbor frequencies of each DNA; in the case of the bacteriophage DNA values, averages of the λ and λ dg sums and of the T2, T4, and T6 sums are given in this table.

* A, T, G, and C refer to the bases adenine, thymine, guanine, and cytosine, respectively.

four-letter alphabet of the four bases, the sequence of the bases spelling out the message. At present we do not know the sequence; what Sanger has done for peptide sequence in protein remains to be done for nucleic acids.

We have approached this problem by developing a method for determining what we call the "nearest-neighbor" base sequences in DNA.[35] DNA is enzymatically synthesized by using one nucleoside triphosphate labeled with phosphorus-32; the other three are unlabeled. The radioactive phosphorus attached to the 5-carbon of the deoxyribose then becomes the bridge between that substrate molecule and the nucleotide at the growing end of the chain with which the substrate reacted (Fig. 9). At the end of the synthetic reaction (after some 10^{16} diester bonds have been formed) the DNA is isolated and digested enzymatically to yield the 3'-deoxynucleotides quantitatively. The phosphorus atom formerly attached to the 5-carbon of the deoxynucleoside triphosphate substrate is now attached to the 3-carbon of the nucleotide with which the substrate reacted during the synthesis of the DNA chains. The phosphorus-32 content of each of the 3'-deoxynucleotides, isolated by paper electrophoresis, is a measure of the relative frequency with which a particular substrate reacted with each of the four nucleotides in the synthesis of the DNA. This procedure, carried out four times with a different labeled substrate in each case, yields the relative frequencies of all the 16 possible kinds of dinucleotide (nearest-neighbor) sequences.

This procedure has been applied to a variety of DNA samples and a few examples of the results are shown. The nearest-neighbor frequencies for *Mycobacterium phlei* DNA are in Table 3. Three points are made from these data.

Replication of the Nucleotide Composition. The first point, shown in the sums of each of four columns, is that

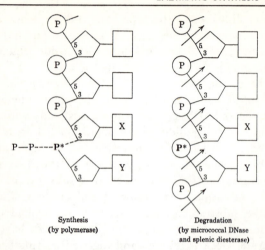

Fig. 9. Synthesis of a P^{32}-labeled DNA chain and its subsequent enzymatic degradation to 3'-deoxyribonucleotides. The arrows indicate the linkages cleaved by micrococcal DNase and calf-spleen phosphodiesterase, yielding a digest composed exclusively of 3'-deoxyribonucleotides.

the incorporation of deoxyadenylate is equal to deoxythymidylate and incorporation of deoxyguanylate is equal to deoxycytidylate; the ratio of incorporation of purine nucleotides to pyrimidine nucleotides is exactly that of the chemical composition of the primer DNA as isolated from nature. These results validate the assumptions in the analytical method and its execution; they also indicate that in each of these experiments faithful replication of the over-all composition of the primer DNA has been achieved.

Base Pairing and Opposite Polarity of Strands. The second point is that these data establish in the enzymatically synthesized DNA the base pairing of the Watson and Crick model and the opposite polarity of the two strands. In

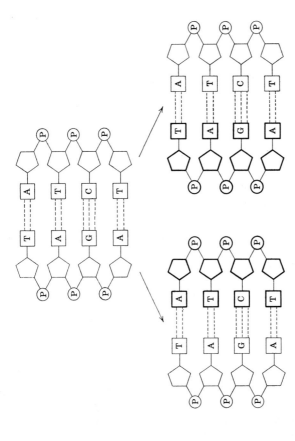

Fig. 10. Proposed scheme of replication of a Watson and Crick DNA model. Boldlined polynucleotide chains of the two daughter molecules represent newly synthesized strands.

TABLE 3

Nearest Neighbor Frequencies of *Mycobacterium phlei* DNA *

Reaction No.	Labeled Triphosphate	Isolated 3'-Deoxyribonucleotide			
		Tp	Ap	Cp	Gp
1	dATP^{32}	a TpA 0.012	b ApA 0.024 I	c CpA 0.063 II	d GpA 0.065 III
2	dTTP^{32}	b TpT 0.026 I	a ApT 0.031	d CpT 0.045 IV	c GpT 0.060 V
3	dGTP^{32}	e TpG 0.063 II	f ApG 0.045 IV	g CpG 0.139	h GpG 0.090 VI
4	dCTP^{32}	f TpC 0.061 III	e ApC 0.064 V	h CpC 0.090 VI	g GpC 0.122
	Sums	0.162	0.164	0.337	0.337

As described in the text, identical Roman numerals designate those sequence frequencies that should be equivalent in a Watson and Crick DNA model with strands of opposite polarity; identical lower-case letters designate sequence frequencies that should be equivalent in a model with strands of similar polarity. The symbol TpA stands for deoxyadenylyl-(5'-3') deoxythymidine.

* Chemical analysis of the base composition of the primer DNA indicated molar proportions of thymine, adenine, cytosine, and guanine of 0.165, 0.162, 0.335, and 0.338, respectively.

the Watson and Crick model two polynucleotide strands are held together in a helix by hydrogen bonds between adenine and thymine and between guanine and cytosine. It was proposed that each strand could serve as a template for the formation of a new polynucleotide chain, the alignment of nucleotides in the new chain being mediated by the same hydrogen-bonding forces (Fig. 10). The postulated scheme allows for precise replication, since one parent helix gives rise to two daughter helices identical to one another and to the parent molecule. Replication of base composition of the primer in the enzymatic synthesis of DNA was presented as evidence for this scheme.[33] Now analysis of the frequencies of nearest-neighbor sequences provides independent support for this mechanism.

The tables show that the amounts of ApA and TpT sequences are equivalent, and so are the frequencies of CpC and GpG sequences (Table 3). It is essential to recognize that matchings of the other sequence frequencies depend upon whether the strands of the double helix are of similar or opposite polarity. For example, the short segments illustrated in Fig. 11 contrast strands of similar polarity with strands of opposite polarity. When we examine the first base sequence T → A (TpA) on the left-hand strand of either double helix, we see at once that the matching sequences predicted by the two models are different. In the opposite polarity model the matching sequence is T → A (TpA), whereas in the similar polarity model the matching sequence is A → T (ApT). In each of the three sequences shown in Fig. 11 (T → A, A → G and G → A) the values are matched by the sequences of the opposite polarity model but not by those of the similar polarity model.

Examination of all the entries in Table 3 shows that there are six matching sequences (indicated by the same Roman numeral) predicted by the model with opposite polarity.

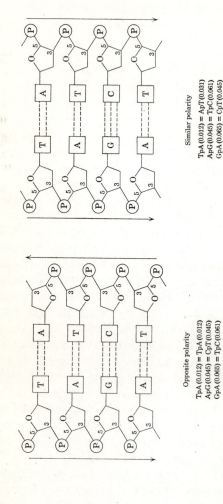

Fig. 11. Contrast of a Watson and Crick DNA model with a model with strands of similar polarity. The predicted matching nearest-neighbor sequence frequencies are different. Values in parentheses are sequence frequencies from the experiment with *M. phlei* DNA. (The strands represented here are the newly synthesized strands of Fig. 10; for ease of comparison, they are aligned as if they were complementary strands of the same double helix.)

In each instance the agreement is good. The four values along the diagonal, which separates the data into two symmetrical halves, are independent and cannot be checked. In other words, every TpA sequence would be matched by a TpA sequence in the complementary strand of opposite polarity; the same constraint would apply to ApT, CpG, and GpC sequences.

In the model with strands of similar polarity the 16 nearest-neighbor sequence frequencies would fall into eight pairs of matching values, indicated in Table 3 by the same lower-case letter. Excluding the ApA, TpT, CpC, and GpG sequences, which match similarly in both models, it is evident that in only four of 12 instances are the values reasonably close. Statistical analysis of the data confirms good fit to the model of opposite polarity but significant deviation from the model of similar polarity.

Nonrandomness of Nearest-Neighbor Frequencies. The third point to be made from these data is the nonrandom nature of the nearest-neighbor frequencies in the enzymatically synthesized DNA. Because there are about 10^4 nearest-neighbor pairs in a DNA strand and perhaps 10^3 or more different strands even in a bacterial DNA population, it was possible that the over-all result would show frequencies predicted by random ordering of the nucleotides in the DNA chains. If this were so, the frequency of a given nearest-neighbor or dinucleotide sequence (e.g., f_{TpA}) in a particular DNA could be predicted from the product of the frequencies of the two constituent mononucleotides (e.g., $f_{Tp} \times f_{Ap}$) in that DNA. Thus the frequencies of sequences ApT and TpA would be equal and predicted by the product $f_{Tp} \times f_{Ap}$. Inasmuch as Ap and Tp occur equally often in DNA, the ApA and ApT sequences would also be equal in frequency. Similarly, the frequencies of the GpA and ApG sequences should on this statistical basis prove to be equal and predicted by the product $f_{Gp} \times f_{Ap}$. The results with all the primers tested show that for every DNA there is significant deviation from the frequencies predicted by random ordering of the mononucleotides. For example, with DNA from *M. phlei,* the TpA sequence occurs only half as often as the ApA sequence. With calf thymus DNA, the CpG sequence occurs less than a third as often as the GpG sequence. The data of each experiment have been statistically analyzed for deviation from perfect fit with the nearest-neighbor frequencies predicted by random arrangement of the mononucleotides. Some general conformity to arrangements expected from the nucleotide composition is observed and is more marked in certain of the DNA's, for example, in the T-even bacteriophages; yet the sequence frequencies for each DNA sample tested are unique and nonrandom in character.

Nearest-Neighbor Sequence Frequencies in Native and Enzymatically Produced DNA; in Bacillus subtilis *DNA.* The nearest-neighbor sequence frequencies measured by the technique in these studies are those in the newly synthesized DNA. The inference that these frequencies are an accurate reflection of those of the native DNA primer was tested in the following way. An enzymatically synthesized sample of "calf thymus" DNA in which only 5% of the total DNA consisted of the native calf thymus primer was itself used as primer in a typical sequence analysis procedure. The results (Table 4) show good agreement between the sequence frequencies of the products primed by the native and the enzymatically synthesized DNA's.

Available physical methods do not enable us to distinguish between DNA samples of identical base composition as, for example, those isolated from a man and a mouse or those from a cow and *B. subtilis.* However, by nearest-neighbor frequency analysis, calf thymus DNA can be dis-

TABLE 4

Nearest Neighbor Frequencies of Native and Enzymatically Synthesized Calf Thymus DNA and of *Bacillus subtilis* DNA

Nearest Neighbor Sequence	Native Calf Thymus DNA (1.25)	Enzymatically Synthesized "Calf Thymus" DNA *	*B. subtilis* DNA (1.29)
ApA, TpT	0.089, 0.087	0.088, 0.083	0.092, 0.095
CpA, TpG	0.080, 0.076	0.078, 0.076	0.067, 0.068
GpA, TpC	0.064, 0.067	0.063, 0.064	0.067, 0.065
CpT, ApG	0.067, 0.072	0.068, 0.074	0.057, 0.058
GpT, ApC	0.056, 0.052	0.056, 0.051	0.048, 0.048
GpG, CpC	0.050, 0.054	0.057, 0.055	0.046, 0.046
TpA	0.053	0.059	0.052
ApT	0.073	0.075	0.080
CpG	0.016	0.011	0.050
GpC	0.044	0.042	0.061

The numbers in parentheses are the

adenine + thymine : guanine + cytosine

ratios determined by chemical analysis.

* Only 5% of this DNA is the native calf thymus primer.

tinguished from *B. subtilis* DNA (Table 4). Most notable in this comparison is the very low value for the CpG sequence in calf DNA. In analyses of 12 animal- and plant-cell DNA's this sequence occurs at a frequency that is invariably far less than that predicted from random association, whereas the frequencies of the isomeric sequence GpC come very close to the expectation for randomness. But in six bacterial DNA samples the reverse of this pattern occurs. Here is a distinction of animal and plant cells from the bacteria which may prove to have phylogenetic significance.

Are the nearest-neighbor sequence patterns in the DNA's from different tissues and tumors of a given species the same? Analyses of bovine sperm, thymus, and liver revealed no variations beyond the error of the method, and similar results were obtained in a comparison of the DNA's of mouse tissues, including two tumors.[36]

Replication of Single-Stranded DNA. The DNA of phage ϕX174 is single-stranded and further distinguished by the absence of equivalence between A and T and between G and C.[23] As mentioned earlier, this DNA is a primer for polymerase and can lead to extensive synthesis of a product with the characteristics of double-stranded DNA.[22] Two nearest-neighbor analyses were carried out, one under conditions of *limited replication* (20% increase over the amount of primer) and the other with *extensive replication* (600% increase).[36]

In *limited replication* DNA synthesis will be directed mainly by original primer molecules and participation of newly synthesized, double-stranded molecules as primers will be minimal. If replication follows the base composition of the primer, the nucleotide composition of the newly synthesized product (identified by its P^{32} label) should be the complement of the base composition of the primer, i.e., the A content of the product should be equal to the T content of the primer, and the T content of the product to the A content of the primer (Fig. 12). The A:T ratio of the product should therefore be the reciprocal of the A:T ratio of the primer. Similarly, the G:C ratio of the product should be the reciprocal of the G:C ratio of the primer. As a consequence, the ratio A + T:G + C of the product should be identical to that of the primer. The results in

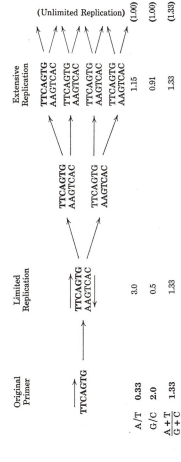

Fig. 12. Scheme for replication of single-stranded DNA. An arbitrarily selected sequence of bases in a hypothetical single-stranded DNA primer is designated in boldface. The base ratios for limited and extensive replication refer to the values for the newly synthesized DNA molecules, designated by standard lightface.

TABLE 5

Composition of Products after Limited and Extensive Replication of ϕX DNA

		Composition Determined by Nearest-Neighbor Analysis				
		20% Synthesis		600% Synthesis		
Base	Composition Determined by Chemical Analysis *	Predicted from Chemical Analysis	Observed	Predicted † from Chemical Analysis	Predicted † from 20% Synthesis	Observed
A	0.246	0.328	0.310	0.287	0.276	0.271
T	0.328	0.246	0.242	0.287	0.276	0.293
G	0.242	0.185	0.202	0.214	0.224	0.213
C	0.185	0.242	0.246	0.214	0.224	0.224

* Reference 23.
† Based on the replication of double-stranded DNA.

Table 5 show that these predictions are fulfilled. The fact that a copy of only 20% of the primer chains is representative of the total can be interpreted in two ways: (1) only one of five molecules primes and is completely replicated, or (2) replication of an average of one fifth of the 5000 nucleotide sequences of *each* molecule is representative of the entire molecule. Density-gradient centrifugation experiments, alluded to earlier, indicating that virtually all (>85%) of the ϕX DNA is combined with new DNA when a 20% increase is reached makes the first interpretation unlikely and the second preferred.

In *extensive replication* the priming molecules after the initial period are double-stranded and accordingly their replication should yield a product with identical nucleotide composition. Specifically, equivalence of purine to pyrimidine nucleotides in the product (A = T, G = C) should obtain, and the A (or T) value, for example, should be equal to one half the sum of the A and T values of the primer (or limited replication product). Thus the mole fraction of A in the original strand was 0.246, that of T, 0.328; consequently the mole fractions in the complementary strand should be 0.328 for A and 0.246 for T. The over-all mole fractions should be A = (0.246 + 0.328)/2 and T = (0.328 + 0.246)/2. These predictions are borne out by the results (Table 5).

Individually the nearest-neighbor frequencies obtained under both conditions of synthesis support the replication mechanism discussed here. Matching of complementary base pairs (in the P^{32}-labeled product) is observed under conditions of *extensive replication* but not in *limited replication* (Table 6). The frequencies of matching nearest-neighbor pairs in *extensive replication* are close to values predicted from the frequencies obtained in *limited replication* by the same reasoning applied to predict over-all base composition in 600% synthesis. Since each of the four sequences TpA, ApT, CpG, and GpC is its own match, the frequencies of each of these sequences should remain unaltered, whether replication is limited or extensive; the results (Table 6) fit this prediction closely.

These data on the replication of $\phi X174$ DNA indicate that the enzymatically synthesized strand primes just as the original strand of phage DNA does and that both strands of a double helix may prime in the enzymatic replication.

Requirement for Four Triphosphates and DNA for DNA Synthesis.

As we have stated earlier, the enzymatic synthesis of DNA requires all four deoxynucleoside triphosphates and DNA. We may formally cite this requirement as another line of evidence for hydrogen bonding as a basis for DNA replication. Without added DNA there is no template for hydrogen bonding, and without all four triphos-

TABLE 6

Nearest-Neighbor Frequencies of ϕX DNA in Limited and in Extensive Replication

Nearest Neighbor Sequence	Limited Replication (20%) Observed	Extensive Replication (600%)	
		Predicted from Limited Replication	Observed
ApA, TpT	0.101, 0.069	0.085, 0.085	0.085, 0.099
CpA, TpG	0.096, 0.048	0.072, 0.072	0.070, 0.070
GpA, TpC	0.054, 0.064	0.059, 0.059	0.058, 0.065
CpT, ApG	0.052, 0.069	0.061, 0.061	0.064, 0.058
GpT, ApC	0.047, 0.068	0.057, 0.057	0.053, 0.053
GpG, CpC	0.040, 0.053	0.046, 0.046	0.041, 0.045
TpA	0.061	0.061	0.059
ApT	0.072	0.072	0.075
CpG	0.045	0.045	0.045
GpC	0.061	0.061	0.061

phates synthesis stops for lack of a hydrogen-bonding mate for each base in the template.

Some Unsolved Questions

What specificity attaches to the size of the primer and does it influence the size of the product? Oligonucleotide mixtures produced by DNase action and chemically synthesized polythymidylates [37] fail to prime the *E. coli* polymerase.* Neither polydeoxynucleotides of intermediate

* Oligonucleotides have been described as primers for terminal addition of nucleotides for the thymus gland polymerase.[38]

size (10^4–10^5 in mol. wt.) nor monodisperse preparations of larger size have been available to us for a proper determination of the influence of primer size.

What is the initial event in enzymatic replication? Does all synthesis start with a covalent (phosphodiester) linkage to the primer or can new chains be started? No evidence has been obtained for initiation of new chains, whereas we do know that covalent bonds are made between the nucleotidyl moiety of the substrate and the nucleoside end of a primer strand. If the latter mechanism prevails, it is not clear how the rigid base-pairing influence of the primer is imposed on the terminal addition of a nucleotide unless the primer loops back on itself.

Does the transforming factor serve as a primer? Although a manyfold increase of DNA obtained from *B. subtilis, Hemophilus influenzae,* or pneumococci is readily demonstrable by chemical analysis, there has been an actual loss in titer of transforming activity due to nuclease activity. Even one break in the thousand-nucleotide long DNA chain might be expected to destroy biological activity. However, collaborative studies with J. Josse, J. Marmur, C. L. Schildkraut, and P. Doty, in which heat-denatured pneumococcal DNA and N^{15}-H^2-*B. subtilis* DNA were used, have yielded suggestive results. With heat-denatured DNA containing the marker for streptomycin resistance a threefold increase in enzymatically synthesized DNA was matched by a threefold increase in transforming-factor activity. Since the biological activity of heat-denatured DNA had been reduced by heating to 6% of the original value, it is uncertain whether the subsequent increase on enzymatic synthesis should be attributed to the "rescue" of inactive strands or to newly synthesized DNA chains. With *B. subtilis* DNA labeled with heavy density markers as primer and unlabeled ("light") deoxynucleoside triphosphates as substrates, an enzymatically synthesized "light" DNA was isolated by CsCl density-gradient sedimentation. This light DNA contained of the order of 100 times more transforming activity per microgram of DNA than could be accounted for by primer DNA in control runs. Here again it is possible that "rescue" and "recombination" processes might have operated to incorporate primer strands into the light DNA fraction. By use of radioactive isotopic markers in the primers, we plan to separate and identify newly synthesized chains and by this means determine whether genetically active DNA molecules free of primer strands have been formed.

Summary and Conclusions

The enzymatic approaches to the problem of DNA replication and the properties of the DNA-synthesizing enzyme purified from *E. coli* have been sketched. The unifying and basic generalization about the action of this enzyme is that it catalyzes the synthesis of a new DNA chain in response to directions from a DNA template; these directions are dictated by the hydrogen-bonding relationship of adenine to thymine and of guanine to cytosine. The experimental basis for this conclusion is derived from the observations of (1) the double-stranded character of the enzymatically synthesized DNA, (2) the pattern of substitution of analogs for the naturally occurring bases, (3) the replication of the chemical composition, (4) the replication of the nucleotide (nearest-neighbor) sequences and the antiparallel direction of the strands, (5) replication of chemical composition and nucleotide sequences of single-stranded DNA, and (6) the requirement for all four deoxynucleoside triphosphates (adenine, thymine, guanine, and cytosine) and DNA primer for DNA synthesis.

REFERENCES

1. Avery, O. T., C. M. MacLeod, and M. McCarty, *J. Exptl. Med.*, **79**, 137 (1944); Hotchkiss, R. D., in *The Chemical Basis of Heredity* (eds. W. D. McElroy and B. Glass), Johns Hopkins Press, Baltimore, 1957, p. 321.
2. Hershey, A. D., *Cold Spring Harbor Symposia Quant. Biol.*, **18**, 135 (1953).
3. Beadle, G. W., in *The Chemical Basis of Heredity* (eds., W. D. McElroy and B. Glass), Johns Hopkins Press, Baltimore, 1957, p. 3.
4. Weiss, S. B., and T. Nakamoto, *J. Biol. Chem.*, **236**, PC 18 (1961); Hurwitz, J., J. J. Furth, M. Anders, P. J. Ortiz, and J. T. August, *J. chim. Phys.*, p. 934 (1961); Stevens, A., *J. Biol. Chem.*, **236**, PC 43 (1961); Ochoa, S., D. P. Burma, H. Kroger, and J. D. Weill, *Proc. Natl. Acad. Sci. U. S.*, **47**, 670 (1961); Hall, B. J., and S. Spiegelman, *Proc. Natl. Acad. Sci. U. S.*, **47**, 137 (1961); Huang, R. C., N. Maheshwari, and J. Bonner, *Biochem. Biophys. Res. Comm.*, **3**, 689 (1960); Chamberlin, M., and P. Berg, *Proc. Natl. Acad. Sci. U. S.*, **48**, 81 (1962); Wood, W. B., and P. Berg, *Proc. Natl. Acad. Sci. U. S.*, **48**, 94 (1962); Jacob, F., and J. Monod, *J. Mol. Biol.*, **3**, 318 (1961); Matthaei, J. H., and M. W. Nirenberg, *Proc. Natl. Acad. Sci. U. S.*, **47**, 1580 (1961); Nirenberg, M. W., and J. H. Matthaei, *Proc. Natl. Acad. Sci. U. S.*, **47**, 1588 (1961); Lengyel, P., J. F. Speyer, and S. Ochoa, *Proc. Natl. Acad. Sci. U. S.*, **47**, 1936 (1961).
5. Chargaff, E., in *Nucleic Acids* (eds., E. Chargaff and J. N. Davidson), Academic Press, New York, 1955, vol. 1, pp. 307–371.
6. Watson, J. D., and F. H. C. Crick, *Nature*, **171**, 737 (1953); *Cold Spring Harbor Symposia Quant. Biol.*, **18**, 123 (1953).
7. Wilkins, M. H. F., *Biochem. Soc. Symposia (Cambridge, Engl.)*, **14**, 13 (1957).
8. Feughelman, M., R. Langridge, W. E. Seeds, A. R. Stokes, H. R. Wilson, C. W. Hooper, M. H. F. Wilkins, R. K. Barclay, and L. D. Hamilton, *Nature*, **175**, 834 (1955).
9. Meselson, M., and F. W. Stahl, *Proc. Natl. Acad. Sci. U. S.*, **44**, 671 (1958).

10. Taylor, J. H., P. S. Woods, and W. L. Hughes, *Proc. Natl. Acad. Sci. U. S.*, **43**, 581 (1957).
11. Sueoka, N., *Proc. Natl. Acad. Sci. U. S.*, **46**, 83 (1960).
12. Cavalieri, L. F., and B. H. Rosenberg, *Biophys. J.*, **1**, 317, 321, 337 (1961).
13. Kornberg, A., in *The Chemical Basis of Heredity* (eds. W. D. McElroy and B. Glass), Johns Hopkins Press, Baltimore, 1957, p. 579; *Revs. Modern Phys.*, **31**, 200 (1959).
14. Kornberg, A., in *Phosphorus Metabolism* (eds., W. D. McElroy and B. Glass), Johns Hopkins Press, Baltimore, 1951, p. 392; *Advances in Enzymol.*, **18**, 191 (1957).
15. Koshland, D. E., Jr., in *The Mechanism of Enzyme Action* (eds., W. D. McElroy and B. Glass), Johns Hopkins Press, Baltimore, 1954, p. 608.
16. Kornberg, A., I. R. Lehman, and E. S. Simms, *Federation Proc.*, **15**, 291 (1956); Kornberg, A., *Harvey Lectures*, Ser. **53**, 83 (1957–58).
17. Lehman, I. R., M. J. Bessman, E. S. Simms, and A. Kornberg, *J. Biol. Chem.*, **233**, 163 (1958).
18. Bollum, F. J., and V. R. Potter, *J. Am. Chem. Soc.*, **79**, 3603 (1957); Harford, C. G., and A. Kornberg, *Federation Proc.*, **17**, 515 (1958); Bollum, F. J., *ibid.*, **17**, 193 (1958); ———, *ibid.*, **18**, 194 (1959); ———, *J. Biol. Chem.*, **234**, 2733 (1959).
19. Bessman, M. J., I. R. Lehman, E. S. Simms, and A. Kornberg, *J. Biol. Chem.*, **233**, 171 (1958).
20. Adler, J., I. R. Lehman, M. J. Bessman, E. S. Simms, and A. Kornberg, *Proc. Natl. Acad. Sci. U. S.*, **44**, 641 (1958).
21. Schachman, H. K., I. R. Lehman, M. J. Bessman, J. Adler, E. S. Simms, and A. Kornberg, *Federation Proc.*, **17**, 304 (1958).
22. Lehman, I. R., *Ann. N. Y. Acad. Sci.*, **81**, 745 (1959).
23. Sinsheimer, R. L., *J. Mol. Biol.*, **1**, 43 (1959).
24. Lehman, I. R., R. L. Sinsheimer, and A. Kornberg, unpublished observations.
25. Aposhian, H. V., and A. Kornberg, *J. Biol. Chem.* **237**, 519 (1962).
26. Bollum, F. J., *J. Biol. Chem.*, **234**, 2733 (1959).
27. Weygand, F., A. Wacker, and H. Dellweg, *Z. Naturforsch.*, **7b**, 19 (1952); Dunn, D. B., and J. D. Smith, *Nature*, **174**, 305 (1954); Zamenhof, S., and G. Griboff, *ibid.*, **174**, 306 (1954).
28. Heinrich, M. R., V. C. Dewey, R. E. Parks, Jr., and G. W. Kidder, *J. Biol. Chem.*, **197**, 199 (1952).
29. Bessman, M. J., I. R. Lehman, J. Adler, S. B. Zimmerman, E. S.

Simms, and A. Kornberg, *Proc. Natl. Acad. Sci. U. S.*, **44**, 633 (1958).
30. Kornberg, A., S. B. Zimmerman, S. R. Kornberg, and J. Josse, *Proc. Natl. Acad. Sci. U. S.*, **45**, 772 (1959).
31. Sinsheimer, R. L., *Science*, **120**, 551 (1954); Volkin, E., *J. Am. Chem. Soc.*, **76**, 5892 (1954); Streisinger, G., and J. Weigle, *Proc. Natl. Acad. Sci. U. S.*, **42**, 504 (1956).
32. Sinsheimer, R. L., *Proc. Natl. Acad. Sci. U. S.*, **42**, 502 (1956); Jesaitis, M. A., *J. Exptl. Med.*, **106**, 233 (1957); *Federation Proc.*, **17**, 250 (1958).
33. Lehman, I. R., S. B. Zimmerman, J. Adler, M. J. Bessman, E. S. Simms, and A. Kornberg, *Proc. Natl. Acad. Sci. U. S.*, **44**, 1191 (1958).
34. Schachman, H. K., J. Adler, C. M. Radding, I. R. Lehman, and A. Kornberg, *J. Biol. Chem.*, **235**, 3242 (1960).
35. Josse, J., A. D. Kaiser, and A. Kornberg, *J. Biol. Chem.*, **236**, 864 (1961).
36. Swartz, M. N., T. A. Trautner, and A. Kornberg, *J. Biol. Chem.* **237**, 1961 (1962).
37. Khorana, H. G., and J. P. Vizsolyi, *J. Am. Chem. Soc.*, **83**, 675 (1961).
38. Bollum, F. J., *J. Biol. Chem.*, **235**, PC 18 (1960).

CHAPTER

2

DE NOVO SYNTHESIS OF
DNA-LIKE POLYMERS

The DNA-synthesizing enzyme (polymerase) purified from *Escherichia coli* catalyzes the extensive formation of DNA in response to directions from a DNA template. This replication requires the presence of the four deoxynucleoside triphosphates commonly found in DNA and the DNA template.[1] In the absence of one, two, or three of the triphosphates a very slight or limited reaction occurs which represents the addition of only one or a very few deoxynucleotide residues to the deoxynucleoside end of the DNA primer molecule.[2] Both the extensive and limited reactions occur *without lag* and are detectable *only when DNA is present*.

We have observed two reactions that may be regarded as exceptions to this rule. The reactions were observed only after *lag periods* of several hours and occurred *in the absence of added DNA*. The products of the reactions, as judged by viscometric, sedimentation, and spectrophotometric studies, were rod-shaped, double-stranded macromolecules like DNA. In one case the product was a polymer composed exclusively of deoxyadenylate and deoxythymidylate (dAT);[3] in the other it contained only deoxyguanylate and deoxycytidylate (dGdC).[4] When either polymer was isolated and used as a primer in the enzymatic reaction, there was prompt and extensive synthesis of an identical polymer. We shall proceed now to a discussion of the synthesis, properties, and significance of these novel macromolecules.

dAT Copolymer

Time Course of Unprimed (De Novo) Synthesis. When the course of reaction in the absence of primer was followed in the viscometer (Fig. 1), there was an initial lag period, then a rapid synthesis until 60 to 80% of the deoxynucleoside triphosphates were utilized, and finally a period (presumably coincident with exhaustion of one of the substrates) of polymer degradation by nucleases to nonviscous, acid-soluble products. The same kinetics were also observed with spectrophotometric or radioisotope incorporation methods. The synthesis depends on the presence of polymerase, dATP, dTTP and Mg^{2+}. The lag period is, within limits, a function of the amount of polymerase present.

Priming Activity of Product of De Novo Synthesis. When the product was isolated from an unprimed reaction and incubated with polymerase, dATP, dTTP and Mg^{2+}, there was a *prompt* synthesis of polymer (Fig. 2). As will become apparent later in a discussion of the mechanism of dAT synthesis, all of the observable changes in an unprimed reaction are in fact the replication of high molecular weight dAT formed *de novo* during the lag period.

With a primer containing only A and T at hand, we could explore the specificity of the limited reaction carried

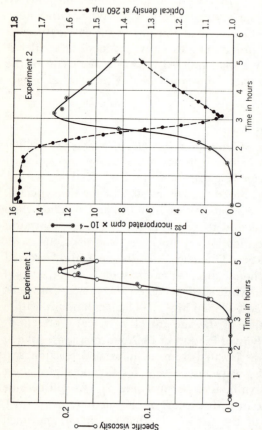

Fig. 1. Course of synthesis of dAT as measured by viscometry, spectrophotometry, and radioisotope incorporation. The reaction mixtures contained in a volume of 1 ml: potassium phosphate buffer, pH 7.4; MgCl$_2$; dTTP, 0.3 μmole; dATP^{32}, 0.3 mole; enzyme, about three units. No DNA was present. Absorbance was measured in the spectrophotometer with a light path reduced to 2.99 mm and a blank, the absorption of which at 260mμ was 0.46. All reactions were carried out at 37°.

DE NOVO SYNTHESIS OF DNA-LIKE POLYMERS

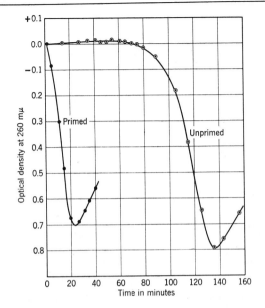

Fig. 2. Comparison of primed versus unprimed synthesis of dAT. The reaction mixtures contained in 0.3 ml: potassium phosphate buffer, pH 7.4; MgCl$_2$; 30 mµmoles each of dATP and dTTP; and 1.5 units of polymerase. The primed reaction contained, in addition, 0.05 ml of a solution of dAT with an optical density at 260 mµ of 2.32. Absorbency measurements were made at 37° in the spectrophotometer with a blank, the absorption of which at 260 mµ was 1.05.

out with a single deoxynucleoside triphosphate. With calf thymus DNA as primer, we had observed that any one of the four substrates is active and the primer is lengthened by one or a few nucleotide residues.[2] With dAT as primer, we found that either A or T alone is incorporated into polymer to the extent of one or two residues per polymer chain of 10,000 residues (molecular weight $c.\ 3 \times 10^6$). This incorporation was dependent on the presence of dAT copolymer, and, of greatest interest, there was no detectable incorporation of dCTP or dGTP. These results suggest, in conjunction with other interpretations of polymerase action (Chapter 1), that the incorporation of a single deoxyribonucleotide is not a haphazard addition to the end of a primer chain. Instead, it is governed by the hydrogen-bond pairing of adenine to thymine and guanine to cytosine; for lack of guanine or cytosine in the dAT copolymer, neither dCTP nor dGTP can be incorporated.

Characterization of dAT Copolymer. The product of an unprimed or primed reaction contains equal amounts of adenine and thymine, even if all four deoxynucleoside triphosphates are present; guanine or cytosine are not incorporated. Thus the polymer fulfills the requirement of the base-pairing implicit in the Watson-Crick double-stranded model for DNA (see Chapter 1). What is the primary structure of the polymer? It could consist of chains with only A and chains with only T. Alternatively, a chain could contain both A and T. To determine the sequential arrangement of A and T, a nearest-neighbor frequency analysis was carried out (Chapter 1). The frequencies of ApT and TpA were each 0.500, whereas the sequences ApA and TpT were undetectable (<0.001). Thus dAT is a copolymer of A and T in an alternating sequence with few if any sequences in which A is covalently bonded to another A or T to another T.

Calculations of the molecular weight from sedimentation values (14 to 28S) and reduced viscosities (9 to 26 dl/g) yielded values of 2 to 8×10^6. The physical data, particularly the high reduced viscosities, suggest that the macromolecules are organized as relatively stiff particles with effective volumes substantially greater than would be expected

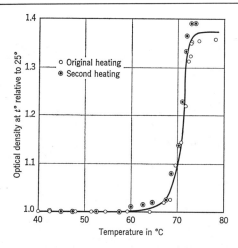

Fig. 3. Melting of dAT copolymer. Plotted on the abscissa is the relative absorbency at 260 mμ at $t°$ compared to the value at 25°. The ordinate gives the temperature. The first heating cycle is indicated by open circles, and the solution after cooling in the stoppered cell was heated a second time, giving the data indicated. The absorbency of the solution of polymer was 0.325 at 25°. The dAT copolymer had been prepared in a *de novo* synthesis and had a reduced viscosity of 30 (g/100 ml)$^{-1}$ and a sedimentation coefficient of 17S. The solvent was 0.2M NaCl and 0.1M sodium citrate.

from single polynucleotide chains with freedom of rotation at each link in the backbone. In support of this view, we observed that the dAT copolymer melted sharply at 71° (Fig. 3), with an increase of 37% in the absorbency at 260 mμ. It can be inferred from these results that the dAT copolymer is a two-stranded structure involving hydrogen bonds between the adenine residues in one chain and the thymine moieties in the second.

Unlike natural DNA, however, the melting of the dAT copolymer upon heating and subsequent reformation upon

Fig. 4. Electron micrograph of dAT. The specimens were shadowed with platinum, and 880-A latex spheres were added to allow calculation of the magnification and shadow to height ratio. Diameter of dAT in a direction normal to the substrate is 10 to 20 A. An Hitachi Model HU-10 microscope was used. (Courtesy of R. B. Inman and R. L. Baldwin.)

DE NOVO SYNTHESIS OF DNA-LIKE POLYMERS

cooling were completely reversible, as shown by the data in Fig. 3. These results agree with those of Marmur and Doty,[5] and, as they suggested, the recovery of a fully hydrogen-bonded structure by dAT as contrasted with DNA can be attributed to the alternation in the sequence of deoxyadenylate and deoxythymidylate in the chains. Upon cooling of melted DNA molecules, only a fraction of the

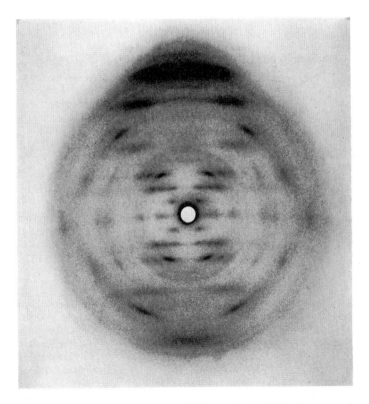

Fig. 5. X-ray diffraction pattern of lithium salt of dAT. (Courtesy of D. R. Davies and R. L. Baldwin.)

bases can be paired correctly to give a partial organization involving hydrogen bonds between the purines and pyrimidines. With dAT, however, the base pairing can be much more complete to give a molecule that is similar to the unheated polymer.

Additional evidence that dAT is a long fibrous molecule is provided by electron micrographs (Fig. 4). X-ray diffrac-

TABLE 1

Relationship between Extent of Reaction and Size of Product

Experiment	Extent of Reaction		Properties of Product	
	Viscosity	Hypo-chromicity	Sedimentation Coefficient	Reduced Viscosity
		%	S	(g/100 ml)$^{-1}$
1	8	5	29	
	37	46	28	26
	100	100	27	24
2	36	28	19	23
	80	91	19	25
	100	100	20	26

Relationship between size of dAT copolymer and extent of *de novo* synthesis. Reaction mixture, 6 ml, was incubated directly in viscometers; at selected times after the viscosity of the solution had been measured aliquots were removed and the enzymatic action terminated by the addition of NaCl-citrate solution to give a concentration of $0.2M$ NaCl-$0.1M$ sodium citrate. Absorbency measurements of these samples as compared to the original gave a measure of the extent of the reaction (hypochromicity). The samples were then dialyzed, and the reduced viscosity, η_{sp}/c, in (g/100 ml)$^{-1}$ and sedimentation coefficient were measured in $0.2M$ NaCl and $0.1M$ sodium citrate.

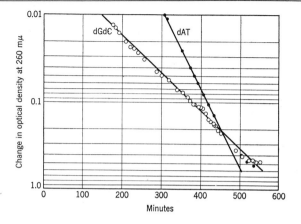

Fig. 6. Semilogarithmic plot of *de novo* AT synthesis.

tion patterns of the lithium salt of dAT (Fig. 5) are indistinguishable from those of lithium salts of natural DNA.

Size of Polymer during De Novo Synthesis. The development of dAT did not proceed by continuous lengthening of polymer molecules until the substrates were exhausted. Instead, we found that the size of the polymers when only 5% of the full hypochromic effect had been attained was the same as those isolated at the end of the reaction (Table 1). It is clear that macromolecules were formed early and that available substrate molecules were used for replication of additional polymer molecules whose average size remained constant.

Kinetics of De Novo and Primed Synthesis. The kinetics of *de novo* dAT synthesis were exponential from the earliest measurements until as much as 65% of the substrates had been consumed [6] (Fig. 6). Exponential kinetics in the phase of rapid synthesis, where the bulk of the reaction occurred,

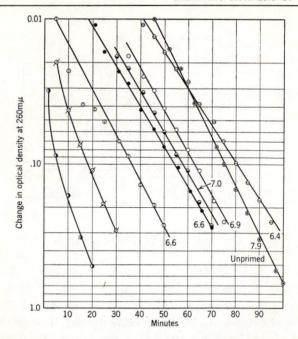

Fig. 7. Semilogarithmic plots of primed dAT reactions.

suggests that the autocatalytic process may originate in the lag period, where it is obscured by the relative insensitivity of the methods used for measuring synthesis. In fact, exponential kinetics might prevail throughout most of the lag period. The kinetics of primed synthesis support this idea.

Semilogarithmic plots of five dAT-primed reactions covering a tenfold range in primer concentrations yielded straight lines with virtually identical slopes (Fig. 7; see also k values in Table 2). These results indicate only that the reactions were autocatalytic over that range of reaction in which accurate spectrophotometric measurements could be made (as in *de novo* synthesis). However, if the reactions were autocatalytic from the very appearance of polymer, it should be possible (by using the exponential rate equation and k determined from the semilogarithmic plots) to calculate the length of the lag period for any concentration of primer. Such a comparison of observed and calculated

TABLE 2

Comparison of Experimental and Calculated Parameters in Primed dAT Synthesis

Experiment	$k \times 10^2$ (min^{-1})	dAT Primer Concentration			Length of Lag Period [1]		
		I Experimental P_0	II Calculated [2] $(P_0)_c$	Calculated Experimental	III Experimental t	IV Calculated [3] t_c	Calculated Experimental
		mμmoles/ml			minutes		
1	6.6	1.14×10^{-3}	1.74×10^{-3}	1.53	37.0	44.1	1.19
	6.6	4.54×10^{-4}	4.66×10^{-4}	1.02	57.0	57.8	1.01
	7.0	3.40×10^{-4}	3.35×10^{-4}	0.99	58.5	58.6	1.00
	6.9	2.27×10^{-4}	2.41×10^{-4}	1.06	64.0	65.2	1.02
	6.4	1.14×10^{-4}	1.06×10^{-4}	0.93	82.0	80.8	0.99
2	9.7	2.34×10^{-3}	2.73×10^{-3}	1.17	20.5	23.0	1.12
	10.0	1.17×10^{-3}	1.64×10^{-3}	1.40	25.0	29.0	1.16
	9.6	2.34×10^{-4}	3.56×10^{-4}	1.52	42.0	46.6	1.10

Column I contains the concentration of dAT primer, P_0, used in the experiments, and Column II the calculated concentrations of dAT, $(P_0)_c$, that would result in the observed lag periods listed in Column III.

[1] Lag period is defined here as the time required to use 10% of the substrate (synthesize 20 mμmoles dAT/ml). Column IV lists the calculated times, t_c, required to synthesize 20 mμmoles dAT/ml, starting with the primer concentrations listed in Column I. The first-order rate constant, k, was experimentally determined for each reaction as illustrated in Fig. 10b.

[2] $(P_0)_c = Pe^{-kt}$, $(P_0)_c$ is the calculated amount of primer required to synthesize 20 mμmoles dAT in t minutes, P = total concentration of polymer at time t, = polymer synthesized, P_s, plus primer, P_0. Since $P_s \gg P_0$, $P \cong P_s = 0.02$ μmoles/ml.

[3] $t_c = \frac{1}{k} \ln \frac{P_s + P_0}{P_0}$.

lag times (Table 2, columns III and IV) showed good agreement; so did the more sensitive comparison of calculated and experimental values of initial primer concentration (P_0). These data suggest that primed syntheses are exponential from the very outset; the lag period in *primed* synthesis therefore can be accounted for *entirely* on the basis of autocatalytic kinetics.

Sensitive Detection of De Novo Polymer Synthesis during the "Lag" Phase. The sensitivity of the physical methods used was inadequate for detecting synthesis much below 1% of the total reaction and therefore for studying the lag period. However, by measuring the development of priming or lag-reducing activity, we could demonstrate a progressive reaction during the lag period. At several times during the lag phase aliquots were taken and heated (70° for five minutes) to inactivate polymerase (Fig. 8a). Fresh enzyme was then added to each aliquot and the further course of the reaction was observed spectrophotometrically. It is clear that an aliquot removed at the end of the lag period (Fig. 8b, sample No. 3) showed no further lag, whereas with an aliquot removed in the middle of the lag period (sample No. 2) a further lag period of equal duration ensued. An aliquot removed very early in the lag phase (No. 1) showed no reduction in lag in the subsequent incubation. When aliquots similar to those just described were centrifuged in a swinging bucket rotor at $125,000 \times g$ for seven hours, all the lag-reducing activity was recovered from the bottom part of the tube. This sedimentation behavior, resembling as it does the properties of dAT, suggests that a polymer of large size was produced during the first fifth of the lag period.

These data indicate that dAT * was synthesized very

* The enzyme preparations contained no dAT as judged by the absence of sedimentable lag-reducing activity.

DE NOVO SYNTHESIS OF DNA-LIKE POLYMERS

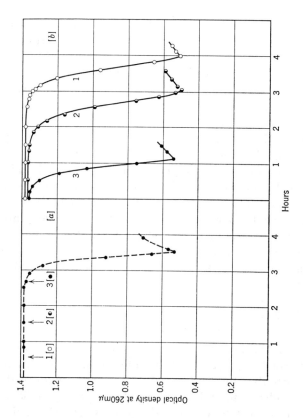

Fig. 8. Lag-reducing activity produced during lag phase.

early in the lag period and that the further time course of synthesis followed largely from the autocatalytic replication of the few macromolecules produced *de novo*. We have calculated from experiments like those in Fig. 7 that midway in the lag period the concentration of dAT was $2 \times 10^{-13} M$ (assuming a molecular weight of $c.\ 3 \times 10^6$) while that of polymerase was $2 \times 10^{-8} M$. The enzyme was therefore in excess of the polymer at this point by a factor of 10^5. The reaction in this instance remained exponential until two thirds of the substrate was utilized, at which time the enzyme was no longer in appreciable excess.

What remains obscure are the initial events in an unprimed synthesis, i.e., the mechanism of *de novo* development of the dAT polymer. We imagine that the polymer is started by a number of chance interactions of nucleotides catalyzed by the enzyme and that some product possessing a simple and highly regular structure is then favored for further growth. Ordered polymerization continues until the molecule reaches a size suitable for priming. Upon its replication, each of the daughter molecules then becomes a template for further replication in semiconservative fashion (Chapter 1).

dGdC Polymer

De Novo and Primed Synthesis. With polymerase, dGTP, dCTP, and Mg^{2+} in a reaction mixture, but without added primer, a polymer developed following the same time course described for synthesis of dAT.[4] The length of the lag responded to several variables in the same way as the lag period in dAT synthesis and the progress of the reaction could be observed by spectrophotometry, viscometry, or the incorporation of radioactivity into an acid-insoluble product. The concentrations of substrates and enzyme required were several times greater than required for *de novo* dAT

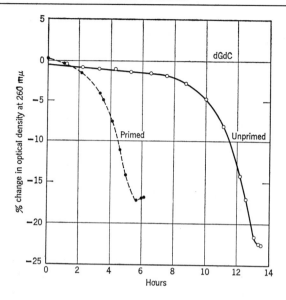

Fig. 9. dGdC synthesis: *de novo* and primed.

synthesis, and this may account for our earlier failure to observe synthesis of a GC-containing polymer.

The isolated product of a *de novo* synthesis was an excellent primer leading without delay to extensive net synthesis of identical polymers (Fig. 9). Further studies of primed synthesis will be mentioned after we consider the structure of the polymer.

Characterization of dGdC Polymer. Analyses of 16 preparations showed only seven with equivalent amounts of deoxyguanylate and deoxycytidylate; the remainder had deoxyguanylate in excess, with molar percentages ranging from 56 to 81. This was in sharp contrast to dAT, with its equivalence of adenine to thymine. Also unlike dAT, this polymer consisted of polydeoxyguanylate strands hydrogen-bonded to chains of polydeoxycytidylate. Nearest-neighbor frequency analysis showed deoxyguanylate always adjacent to deoxyguanylate and deoxycytidylate always a neighbor of deoxycytidylate. Mild acid hydrolysis of the primer [7] released all the deoxyguanylate but none of the deoxycytidylate residues into an acid-soluble form. Thus the dGdC polymer is composed of *homo*polymers of deoxyguanylate and homopolymers of deoxycytidylate. It contains no covalent linkages of deoxyguanylate to deoxycytidylate.

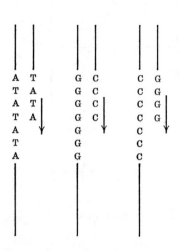

Fig. 10. dGdC structure versus dAT.

Further confirmation of this structure for dGdC comes from its behavior as a primer. The incorporation of dGTP was about the same, whether or not dCTP was present; similarly the incorporation of dCTP was not substantially affected by the presence of dGTP. It is clear that according to the proposed structure for dGdC (Fig. 10), and in distinction to that of dAT, growth of polydeoxyguanylate chains does not require deoxycytidylate residues nor does growth of polydeoxycytidylate chains require deoxyguanylate units.

Sedimentation and viscosity measurements of dGdC yielded values in the range observed for dAT. The helix-coil transition induced by heating was revealed as a sharp "melting" curve with a midpoint (T_m) at 83° (Fig. 11). The difference between this value and the T_m for dAT agrees with the predictions of Marmur and Doty[5] relating T_m to the guanine and cytosine content of DNA. As with dAT, there was an apparent recovery of the hydrogen-bonded structure.

Alkaline titration of dGdC also led to a sharp hyperchromic change which was largely reversible on back-titra-

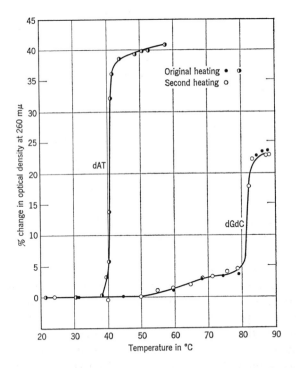

Fig. 11. dGdC melting curve. The solvent contained 0.001M Na$_2$EDTA, 0.005M NaH$_2$PO$_4$, and 0.0025M Na$_2$HPO$_4$ (pH 6.5, ionic strength c. 0.015).

tion. Measured viscometrically, the transition was superimposable on the observed optical changes; however, the changes were irreversible, indicating a failure to resume the original helical structure.

Mechanism of De Novo and Primed Synthesis. As with *de novo* dAT synthesis, the dGdC polymer isolated early in the reaction appeared to have the same average size as that found late in the reaction. The kinetics of primed reactions are exponential throughout their course, as are the kinetics of the measurable course of *de novo* synthesis. Although the studies with dGdC are at this point more limited than those with dAT, they point to similar conclusions: *de novo* synthesis of a few macromolecules early in the lag phase is followed by an autocatalytic replication of these primers until they are no longer limiting.

That the polymers whose *de novo* synthesis has been observed to date have such simple and well-ordered rather than random structures does not seem surprising. The alternating copolymer of A and T and the homopolymers of G and C are the polymers encountered in the reaction mixtures, and we wonder at the absence of the analogous alternating copolymers of G and C and the paired homopolymers of A and T. However, our speculations on the factors responsible for these *de novo* reactions are best deferred at this time. We are hopeful that the intensive physicochemical studies of these polymers by Baldwin and his associates [8,9] will provide one approach to the solution. Another approach will be possible when larger quantities of a more purified polymerase are available. Then, as in studies of the *de novo* synthesis of glycogen by muscle phosphorylase,[10] sensitive measurements may detect development of the polymer directly on the enzyme molecule.

Analogs of the dAT and dGdC Polymers and Their Uses. With dAT and dGdC as primers, analogous polymers have been prepared which contain bromouracil (BU) in place of thymine, bromocytosine (BC) or hydroxymethylcytosine (HMC) in place of cytosine, or hypoxanthine in place of guanine (Table 3). The dAT and dGdC polymers are useful for evaluating properties of DNA which accrue from its base composition. The analogs enlarge the scope of these opportunities, provide specific markers, and confer new chemical properties which may be exploited. We discuss the use of dA$\overline{\text{BU}}$ to produce and study hybrid helices later in some detail. At this point some other examples are cited briefly.

By using dA$\overline{\text{BU}}$ as a primer, we explored the possibility that bromouracil substitutions for thymine might lead to matching errors and so produce mutant copies of the polymer chains. The incorporation of bromouracil into viral

TABLE 3

Enzymatically Synthesized Polymers

Designation	Components *	Reference
Copolymers:		
dAT	Adenylate, thymidylate	3
dA$\overline{\text{BU}}$	Adenylate, bromouridylate	8, 9
Homopolymers:		
dGdC	Guanylate, cytidylate	4
dIdC	Inosinate, cytidylate	†
dGd$\overline{\text{BC}}$	Guanylate, bromocytidylate	4
dGd$\overline{\text{HMC}}$	Guanylate, hydroxymethylcytidylate	‡

* All the components are deoxyribonucleotides.
† R. B. Inman and R. L. Baldwin, unpublished observation.
‡ J. Josse and A. Kornberg, *J. Biol. Chem.*, **237**, 1968 (1962).

or bacterial DNA is known to be associated with an increase in the mutation rate. Mutations resulting from occasional pairing of guanine with tautomeric forms of thymine or bromouracil that resemble cytosine have been suggested by Watson and Crick [11] and Freese.[12] Matching of bromouracil with guanine instead of with adenine leads, in subsequent replications, to a G-C pair in place of an original A-T. Would the presence of bromouracil in a DNA primer increase the incidence of "incorporation errors" when the DNA is enzymatically replicated? We [13] first established that replication of dAT incorporated no guanine (less than one guanine residue incorporated per 28,000 to 580,000 adenine and thymine nucleotides polymerized). However with dA$\overline{\text{BU}}$ as primer, guanine incorporation occurred at a frequency of one residue per 2000 to 25,000 adenine and thymine nucleotides polymerized. Although nearest-neighbor analysis of the incorporated guanine residues is not explained simply by mismatching with bromouracil, the influence of dA$\overline{\text{BU}}$ in producing "aberrant" guanine incorporation is unequivocal.

In studying the biosynthesis of T-even phage DNA's, we are concerned with the mechanism that directs the specific glucosylation patterns that characterize and distinguish these phages (Chapter 3). Using dGd$\overline{\text{HMC}}$ polymer as glucose acceptor, we found that specific glucosyl transferases could glucosylate up to 35% of the HMC residues. This finding establishes that HMC residues in long runs, which therefore lack any other bases as nearest neighbors, are susceptible to this extent to glucosylation.

Several other recent or imminent uses of these polymers should be mentioned. These include their application in biophysical studies of helix-coil transitions dependent on temperature and pH,[8] optical dichroism,[14] density gradient sedimentation,[5,8,9] ultraviolet light inactivation and enzymatically catalyzed photoreversal, and formation of hybrids with RNA-like polymers.[15] The dAT polymer has been helpful not only in studies of replication by DNA polymerase (Chapter 1) but also in establishing that RNA polymerase functions in a similar fashion.[16] Investigations of the specificities and distinguishing features of nucleases will surely rely in considerable measure on various of these model polymers.[4,17]

Formation of Hybrid Molecules from Two Polymers. In our current view of DNA replication based on the Watson and Crick model each strand of the double helix is copied separately. Separation of the strands takes place either before or coincident with the copying process. Interpretation of the Meselson and Stahl experiments with *E. coli*,[18] which support this semiconservative replication model, rest on the orderly separation of strands of the parent helix and the production of hybrids between one of the parent strands and a newly synthesized complementary strand. Definitive physicochemical evidence for strand separation and hybridization is now needed to verify these interpretations and to provide a firm experimental and theoretical basis for the replication process. The important discoveries from Doty's laboratory [19,20] on the melting and reunion of transforming DNA's represent a long stride in this direction. The investigations by Baldwin, Inman, and Wake [8,9] with the dAT and dA$\overline{\text{BU}}$ polymers, which are reviewed here, bring us still closer to understanding the mechanics of strand separation and helix formation.

Baldwin et al., had first to describe the melting behavior for dAT, dA$\overline{\text{BU}}$, and a mixture of these polymers (Fig. 12). These polymers revealed sharply differing thermal stabilities in a solvent of low ionic strength but did not differ

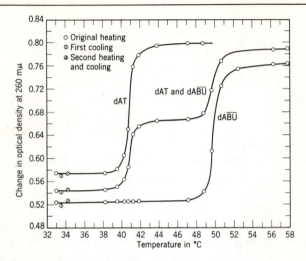

Fig. 12. Melting of dAT, dA$\overline{\text{BU}}$, and a mixture of dAT and dA$\overline{\text{BU}}$. (Courtesy of R. B. Inman and R. L. Baldwin.)

in a high-salt medium. By melting a mixture of these polymers in a high-salt medium and by cooling it slowly through the temperature interval in which the random coil to helix transition occurs, a hybrid polymer was produced (Fig. 13). High concentrations were needed to form the dAT:dA$\overline{\text{BU}}$ hybrid, suggesting that at low concentrations the randomly coiled single strands fold back on themselves rather than interact with other loose strands. Evidence for the existence of a hybrid polymer came first from its distinctive (and predicted) buoyant density in density-gradient sedimentation. As seen in Fig. 14, a new component with a buoyant density intermediate between dAT (density = 1.40) and dA$\overline{\text{BU}}$ (density = 1.57) appeared. The melting behavior of the hybrid isolated in a preparative density-gra-

DE NOVO SYNTHESIS OF DNA-LIKE POLYMERS

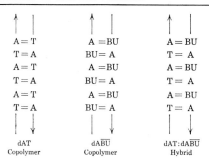

Fig. 13.

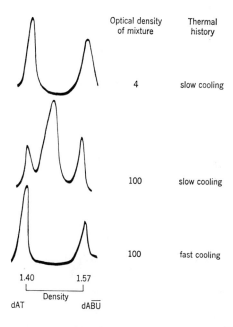

Fig. 14. Density gradient patterns of melted dAT and dA$\overline{BU}$ mixture. (Courtesy of R. Inman and R. L. Baldwin.)

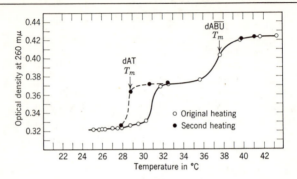

Fig. 15. UV absorption melting curve for dAT:dA$\overline{\text{BU}}$ hybrid. (Courtesy of R. Inman and R. L. Baldwin.)

dient sedimentation was also distinctive, with a T_m between dAT and dA$\overline{\text{BU}}$ (Fig. 15). As interpreted by Inman and Baldwin (Fig. 16),[8] the first hyperchromic step was due to melting of the hybrid bonds; simultaneous realignment of the dA$\overline{\text{BU}}$ strand occurred which then melted at the higher temperature corresponding to the dA$\overline{\text{BU}}$ double helix. On rapid cooling at these concentrations it might be expected that separate double helices of dAT and dA$\overline{\text{BU}}$ would reform, and the melting curve during the second heating cycle (Fig. 15) confirms this expectation.

Enzymatic synthesis of a dAT:dA$\overline{\text{BU}}$ hybrid was demonstrated by Wake and Baldwin,[9] using either dAT or dA$\overline{\text{BU}}$ as primers (Fig. 17). In the dAT-primed reaction with dATP and d$\overline{\text{BU}}$TP as substrates the hybrid appeared at the expense of the primer (Fig. 17, early); with more extensive synthesis, the primer disappeared, the new dA$\overline{\text{BU}}$ product predominated, and a small hybrid component persisted (Fig. 17, late). In the dA$\overline{\text{BU}}$-primed reaction analogous

DE NOVO SYNTHESIS OF DNA-LIKE POLYMERS

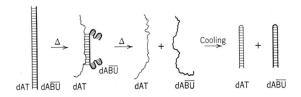

Fig. 16.

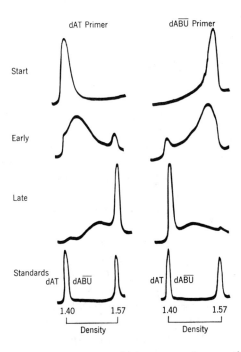

Fig. 17. Density gradient patterns during course of enzymatic synthesis. (Courtesy of R. G. Wake and R. L. Baldwin.)

changes took place. These results and additional studies of the thermal melting of the enzymatically formed hybrid rule out a dispersive mechanism of replication and favor the semiconservative model; however, the possibility of a conservative replication process is not yet excluded.

Does a dAT Copolymer Occur Naturally? Although the conditions for initiating the synthesis of dAT in nature might appear unlikely, the ease of its replication would favor its survival once formed. We were therefore impressed by Sueoka's discovery in crab testis DNA of a separable component with a buoyant density corresponding to dAT and representing 30% of the total DNA.[21] In order to eliminate the possibility that adventitious materials, such as protein, might be responsible for the low buoyant density of this DNA band and with the thought that this component might be a "natural" dAT polymer, Dr. Sueoka asked us to examine these DNA preparations for their nearest-neighbor frequency patterns.

When the light DNA component of crab was tested as a primer for replication, it supported synthesis at a rate comparable to that primed by dAT, but unlike the latter all four deoxynucleoside triphosphates were required.[22] When dGTP and dCTP were omitted, the rate of synthesis was only 19% of that observed with the four triphosphates; when dTTP was also omitted from the incubation mixture, the rate was reduced to less than 0.1%. These results suggested that at least a few G and C residues were interspersed in the chains of the light crab DNA.

Nucleotide incorporation into DNA in the first stage of the nearest-neighbor analysis was in the ratio of A:T:G:C of 0.84:1.07:0.030:0.028 mμmoles, respectively, indicating a G-C content of about 3%. A similar value was obtained by determining the actual nearest-neighbor frequencies (Table 4).

TABLE 4

Comparison of Nearest-Neighbor Frequencies of the Two DNA Components of *Cancer borealis* (Crab) Testis

Nearest-Neighbor Sequence	Main Component (1.80) *	Light Component † (36.6) *
ApA, TpT	0.085, 0.092	0.0127, 0.0126
CpA, TpG	0.067, 0.066	0.0100, 0.0089
GpA, TpC	0.053, 0.054	0.0042, 0.0015
CpT, ApG	0.061, 0.055	0.0004, 0.0018
GpT, ApC	0.057, 0.063	0.0081, 0.0069
GpG, CpC	0.032, 0.038	0.0009, 0.0009
TpA	0.113	0.504
ApT	0.116	0.429
CpG	0.019	0.0007
GpC	0.030	0.0015

* The number in the parenthesis is the $A + T : G + C$ ratio determined by nearest-neighbor analysis.

† Average of two analyses.

The most remarkable result of the nearest-neighbor analysis of the light crab DNA was that alternating A and T residues comprised 93% of the sequences. However, all 16 possible sequences were observed and in a strikingly nonrandom distribution. The matching of sequences conforms to the predictions of Watson-Crick base pairing, except in a few instances in which the low frequencies are technically difficult to measure accurately.

Also included in Table 4 are the nearest-neighbor frequencies determined from the main, heavy component of *Cancer borealis* DNA. The ratio $A + T : G + C$ was 1.8; a value of 1.6 was calculated by Sueoka from the buoyant density. Although the heavy crab DNA showed no gross contamination with the light component, trace amounts might have escaped detection. Since the light component is a better primer, the reaction product of a nearest-neighbor analysis of the heavy component would reveal a relatively higher A + T content (and higher ApT and TpA sequences) than that of the heavy primer.

The possibility might also be considered that the light component is pure dAT and that its contamination by the heavy component is responsible for the presence of the few G and C residues. This is unlikely, however, since replication of the light component, as mentioned, is markedly reduced when G and C are omitted from the reaction mixture. Furthermore, the nearest-neighbor sequences involving G and C are distinctly different in the two DNA components.

The close relationship of the light crab testis DNA to dAT suggests that it may be a natural derivative of this polymer. Questions come to mind regarding the distribution of this type of DNA in various somatic cells and in the sperm of the crab and related species. That the physiologic expression of such a relatively simple DNA may be amenable to analysis is also an intriguing possibility.

Summary and Conclusions

The enzymatic synthesis of novel deoxynucleotide polymers provides an unusual opportunity for learning about the properties of DNA, its replication and perhaps even its *de novo* origin.

In the presence of polymerase, dATP, and dTTP, but in the absence of primer, a polymer of deoxyadenylate (dA) and deoxythymidylate (dT) develops after a lag period. Indications are that *de novo* synthesis of macromolecular primers occurs in the early part of this lag phase and that these molecules are then autocatalytically replicated. The polymer (dAT) is an alternating copolymer of dA and dT residues organized as a double helix with all the physical and chemical properties associated with DNA.

Another polymer (dGdC) synthesized *de novo* by polymerase contains deoxyguanylate (dG) and deoxycytidylate (dC) as homopolymers organized also in a DNA-like structure. With dAT and dGdC as primers, a number of analogous polymers have been prepared which contain bromouracil (d$\overline{BU}$) in place of thymine, bromocytosine or hydroxymethylcytosine in place of cytosine, or hypoxanthine in place of guanine.

This family of relatively simple DNA-like polymers with regularly ordered structures has revealed interesting physicochemical properties, among which are the capacity of a mixture of dAT and dA$\overline{BU}$ polymers to form, under specified conditions, a hybrid containing one strand of dAT and one of dA$\overline{BU}$. Other uses of these polymers as models for biophysical, enzymological, and genetic studies are cited.

In view of the ease with which these simple polymers are replicated by polymerase, are they likely to be found in nature? The remarkable finding that crab testis contains a separable DNA component, which is an alternating copolymer of A and T with a peppering of G and C residues, opens serious and exciting questions about the natural occurrence and physiological significance of these polymers.

REFERENCES

1. Kornberg, A., *Science*, **131**, 1503 (1960).
2. Adler, J., I. R. Lehman, M. J. Bessman, E. S. Simms, and A. Kornberg, *Proc. Natl. Acad. Sci. U. S.*, **44**, 641 (1958).
3. Schachman, H. K., J. Adler, C. M. Radding, I. R. Lehman, and A. Kornberg, *J. Biol. Chem.*, **235**, 3242 (1960).

4. Radding, C. M., J. Josse, and A. Kornberg, *J. Biol. Chem.* (in press).
5. Marmur, J., and P. Doty, *Nature*, **183**, 1427 (1959).
6. Radding, C. M., and A. Kornberg, *J. Biol. Chem.* (in press).
7. Burton, K., and G. B. Peterson, *Biochem. J.*, **75**, 17 (1960).
8. Inman, R. B., and R. L. Baldwin, *J. Mol. Biol.* (in press).
9. Wake, R. G., and R. L. Baldwin, *J. Mol. Biol.* (in press).
10. Illingworth, B., D. H. Brown, and C. F. Cori, *Proc. Natl. Acad. Sci. U. S.*, **47**, 469 (1961); Brown, D. H., B. Illingworth, and C. F. Cori, *Proc. Natl. Acad. Sci. U. S.*, **47**, 479 (1961).
11. Watson, J. D., and F. H. C. Crick, *Viruses, Cold Spring Harbor Symposia*, **18**, 123 (1953).
12. Freese, E., *J. Mol. Biol.*, **1**, 87 (1959).
13. Trautner, T. A., M. N. Swartz, and A. Kornberg, *Proc. Natl. Acad. Sci. U. S.*, **48**, 449 (1962).
14. Gellert, M., *J. Am. Chem. Soc.*, **83**, 4664 (1961).
15. Schildkraut, C. L., J. Marmur, J. R. Fresco, and P. Doty, *J. Biol. Chem.*, **236**, PC 3 (1961).
16. Weiss, S. B., and T. Nakamoto, *Proc. Natl. Acad. Sci. U. S.*, **47**, 1400 (1961); Furth, J. J., J. Hurwitz, and M. Goldmann, *Biochem. Biophys. Res. Comm.*, **4**, 431 (1961); Chamberlin, M., and P. Berg, *Proc. Natl. Acad. Sci. U. S.*, **48**, 81 (1962).
17. Lehman, I. R., G. Roussos, and E. A. Pratt, *J. Biol. Chem.*, **237**, 519 (1962).
18. Meselson, M., and F. W. Stahl, *Proc. Natl. Acad. Sci. U. S.*, **44**, 671 (1958).
19. Doty, P., H. Boedtker, J. R. Fresco, R. Haselkorn, and M. Litt, *Proc. Natl. Acad. Sci. U. S.*, **45**, 482 (1959).
20. Marmur, J., and D. Lane, *Proc. Natl. Acad. Sci. U. S.*, **46**, 453 (1960).
21. Sueoka, N., *J. Mol. Biol.*, **3**, 208 (1961).
22. Swartz, M. N., T. A. Trautner, and A. Kornberg, *J. Biol. Chem.*, **237**, 1961 (1962).

CHAPTER

3

DNA SYNTHESIS IN BACTERIOPHAGE-INFECTED CELLS

Bacteriophages of the T2, T4, and T6 (T-even) series contain DNA enclosed in a protein coat. Upon attachment of the phage to the bacterium, the DNA is injected through the phage tailpiece, and immediately the synthesis of host cell DNA, RNA, and protein ceases. Within two minutes, an RNA specifically related to the phage DNA appears; within four minutes synthesis of special proteins can be detected, and within six minutes phage DNA is synthesized at five times the rate of DNA formation in normal cells. After 20 to 40 minutes, 100 to 200 new phages are produced and released by cell lysis [1] (Fig. 1).

It appears then that the bacterial genome is immobilized by the infection and that all subsequent protein and nucleic-acid synthesis is directed by the phage DNA. In surveying cell-free extracts from various sources for a DNA-synthesizing system, we were attracted to phage-infected cells because very rapid DNA synthesis goes on while other metabolic activities are relatively restricted.[2] We failed at

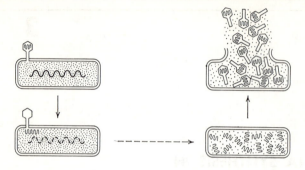

Fig. 1. Life cycle of a T-even bacteriophage.

first to obtain an active extract from infected cells,[3] even after the conditions necessary for DNA synthesis in extracts of uninfected cells were known, for in applying what we knew about DNA synthesis in normal cells to studies of infected cells, the unique features of the phage DNA's posed a number of special problems. The DNA of the T-even phages has hydroxymethylcytosine (HMC) in place of cytosine and contains glucose linked to the HMC groups in ratios characteristic for each type of phage.[4-6] The questions raised by these unusual constituents are the subject headings for this chapter:

1. How is HMC produced in cells that have no enzyme(s) for producing it?
2. Assuming that HMC is incorporated into DNA via HMC deoxynucleoside triphosphate, how is the latter produced in cells that have no phosphorylating (kinase) activity on HMC deoxynucleoside monophosphate?
3. How is cytosine excluded from the phage DNA when cytosine and HMC nucleotides are apparently interchangeable in pairing with guanine?

4. How are the constant and characteristic ratios of glucosylated and nonglucosylated HMC in the phage DNA achieved when glucosylated and nonglucosylated HMC nucleotides are apparently interchangeable in pairing with guanine?

5. Why was the DNA-synthesizing enzyme virtually undetectable in extracts of infected cells, although it is more active than in extracts of uninfected cells?

Synthesis of HMC Deoxynucleoside Monophosphate. Flaks and Cohen showed that within several minutes after infection by phages T2, T4, or T6 a new enzyme is produced which hydroxymethylates deoxycytidylate, according to the reaction: [7]

$$\text{dCMP} + \text{HCHO} \xrightarrow[\text{tetrahydrofolate}]{} \text{d}\overline{\text{HMC}} \text{ monophosphate}$$

We have confirmed this finding as well as the observation that no hydroxymethylase activity occurs in either uninfected cells or in cells infected with phage T5 which has no HMC in its DNA [8] (Fig. 2*f*).

Synthesis of HMC Deoxynucleoside Triphosphate. Extracts of infected cells also contained an enzyme which phosphorylated d$\overline{\text{HMC}}$ monophosphate leading to the synthesis of HMC deoxynucleoside triphosphate [8,9] (Fig. 2*a*). The enzyme (d$\overline{\text{HMCMP}}$ kinase) was first detected four minutes after infection but was not measurable in normal or T5-infected cells. We also observed, as did Bessman independently,[10] that levels of deoxythymidylate and deoxyguanylate kinases were increased twentyfold, although the deoxyadenylate kinase level was essentially unaltered. In both cases the maximal level of kinase activity was reached about 15 minutes after infection when the kinase levels were nearly the same for each of the four nucleotides. Bessman has

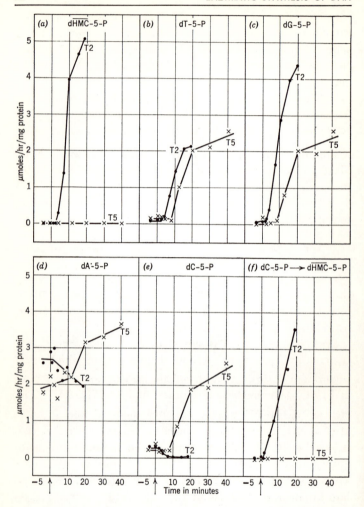

Fig. 2. Deoxynucleotide-phosphorylating enzymes ("kinases") (*a–e*) and hydroxymethylating enzyme (*f*) levels before and after infection with phage T2 or T5. The arrows indicate the start of infection.

made the highly interesting discovery that the deoxyguanylate and deoxythymidylate kinase activities which appear after infection are distinctly different from those present prior to infection.[11] He and his associates [12] also have impressive evidence that the kinase activities for d$\overline{\text{HMC}}$ monophosphate, deoxythymidylate, and deoxyguanylate are not separable and may occur in a single enzyme!

By contrast to the high kinase levels for the four deoxynucleotides that are incorporated into T2 DNA, only traces of deoxycytidylate kinase were detected in infected cells (Fig. 2e). Furthermore, extracts of T2-infected cells inhibited the deoxycytidylate kinase activity of extracts of normal cells when equal amounts of extracts from infected and uninfected cells were mixed. This inhibitory effect is due to a new enzyme (dCTPase) which destroys dCTP [8,13,14] (see below). By using fluoride, which inhibits dCTPase, we could show that there was actually little or no change in the deoxycytidylate kinase level upon infection.[8]

Bacteriophage T5 contains cytosine rather than HMC in its DNA. Infection with this phage produced increased kinase activities for those deoxynucleotides that occur in its DNA (Fig. 2b, c, e). There was a tenfold increase in deoxycytidylate kinase activity in extracts of T5-infected cells, which may be contrasted with the lack of any increase in this activity in the extracts of T2-infected cells.

Exclusion of Cytosine from Incorporation into DNA.

Upon closer study of the apparent inhibition of deoxycytidylate kinase by extracts of T2 phage-infected cells, we [8,14] recognized it to be due to an enzyme which destroys the product of kinase action, namely dCTP, by removal of the terminal pyrophosphate group:

$$dCTP + H_2O \rightarrow dCMP + \text{inorganic pyrophosphate}$$

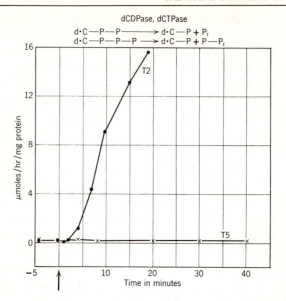

Fig. 3. dCTPase levels before and after infection with phage T2 or T5. The arrow indicates the start of infection. The incubation mixtures (0.25 ml) contained 6.0 mµmoles of dCTP labeled with P^{32} in the terminal pyrophosphate group, glycine buffer, pH 9.2, $MgCl_2$, 2-mercaptoethanol, and 0.3 µg of partially purified enzyme. After 20 min of incubation at 37°, the reaction was terminated by adding HCl. Norit was stirred in, removed by centrifugation, and the supernatant fluid was assayed for radioactivity.

The kinetics of enzyme appearance after infection (Fig. 3) are similar to those already described for hydroxymethylase and the kinases.

The enzyme has been purified and demonstrated to be active only on dCTP among 10 closely related deoxy- and ribonucleoside triphosphates tested. It does not, for example, split d$\overline{\text{HMC}}$TP. The enzyme does, however, split dCDP:

$$dCDP + H_2O \rightarrow dCMP + \text{inorganic orthophosphate}$$

Evidence that a single enzyme is responsible for both dCTP and dCDP cleavage was derived from kinetic measurements, fractionation, and purification steps, sensitivity to fluoride inhibition and other properties.[14]

The dCTPase-dCDPase activity was also identified in extracts of cells infected with T4 and T6 phages but was barely detectable in extracts of uninfected cells or of cells infected with T5. The level of dCTP cleavage in extracts of uninfected cells was approximately 1% of the activity found in extracts of T2-infected cells. However, it was distinguished from the latter activity by its lesser sensitivity to fluoride, lower pH optimum, and greater rate of cleavage of dCDP than dCTP. It therefore seems probable that the infected cell dCTPase-dCDPase is totally absent from uninfected cells.

The dCDP- and dCTP-splitting activity measured after phage infection was of the order of 60 times greater than the deoxycytidylate kinase activity. Considering the tight binding of these substrates by the cleavage enzyme ($K_m = c.\ 3 \times 10^{-6}M$), this finding is consistent with the known events of infection. Assuming for the moment that the polymerase in infected cells cannot distinguish between the deoxynucleoside triphosphates of C and HMC, this dCTP-splitting enzyme provides a reasonable mechanism for excluding cytosine from phage DNA (Fig. 4).

The phosphorylation of deoxycytidylate in *Escherichia coli* almost certainly involves the intermediate production of dCDP [15] so that the dCDP-splitting activity would thus allow another stage at which the production of dCTP could be

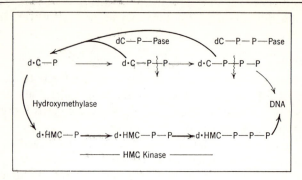

Fig. 4.

diverted. The product of either dCDP or dCTP cleavage is dCMP, the substrate for hydroxymethylase. This leads, as already mentioned, via the d$\overline{\text{HMC}}$MP kinase action to d$\overline{\text{HMC}}$TP. The latter nucleotide is insusceptible to cleavage by the dCTP-splitting enzyme and, as we shall see, is readily incorporated into phage DNA.

Synthesis of Glucosylated HMC Residues in DNA. According to our understanding of DNA synthesis by the polymerase system obtained from normal *E. coli,* it is difficult to conceive how the constant glucose:HMC ratio which characterizes each phage DNA is achieved if the incorporation were to occur via glucosylated and nonglucosylated HMC nucleotides. Is there a mechanism for direct glucosylation of the DNA even though direct substitutions on intact DNA have been hitherto unknown?

In extracts of T2-infected cells we observed an enzyme that transfers glucose from uridine diphosphate glucose (UDP glucose) to HMC residues in DNA.[8] (The HMC-containing DNA acceptor in this instance was enzymatically prepared with purified polymerase using d$\overline{\text{HMC}}$TP in place of dCTP.) Like the other phage-induced enzymes discussed earlier the glucosyl transferase appears at about the same time during the course of a T2-infection and is undetectable in extracts of normal or T5-infected cells (Fig. 5). When DNA, enzymatically prepared with dCTP instead of dHMCTP, was tested as an acceptor or when the glucosylated DNA from phage T2 itself was used, no glucose transfer to DNA was measurable. The HMC mono- and

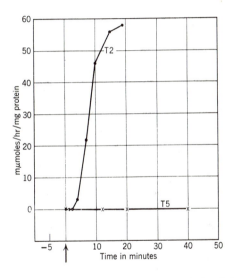

Fig. 5. DNA-glucosylating enzyme levels before and after infection with phage T2 or T5. The arrow indicates the start of infection. The incubation mixtures (0.20 ml) contained 10 mμmoles of UDP glucose labeled uniformly with C^{14} in the glucose residue, Tris buffer, pH 7.5, glutathione, DNA synthesized enzymatically (using thymus or phage T2 DNA as primer) and containing about 1 mμmole of HMC, and extract containing 10 to 50 μg of protein. After 15 min of incubation at 30°, the mixture was treated as in the "polymerase" assay of incorporation of a labeled deoxynucleotide into an acid-insoluble product.

triphosphates failed to substitute for HMC-containing DNA as glucose acceptors.

The work of several investigators had indicated a characteristic glucose: HMC ratio for each phage [5,6] and with the recent analyses by Lehman and associates [16,17] the nature and percentage distribution of the glucosyl HMC groups can be described as follows:

	T2	T4	T6
Unglucosylated	25	0	25
α-Glucosyl	70	70	3
β-Glucosyl	0	30	0
β-Glucosyl-α-glucosyl (gentiobiosyl)	5	0	72

What determines these characteristic glucosylation patterns in each of the phage DNA's? Is it determined by the nucleotide sequence in the particular DNA that influences the action of a single glucosylating enzyme? Are there different enzymes which develop in each particular phage infection? It is now clear that highly specific glucosyl transferases are developed in response to infection with T2, T4, or T6 phages and that these enzymes account in large measure for the distinctive distribution of glucose residues in the DNA of each phage. However, the way in which DNA structure determines the rate and extent of reaction with each kind of glucosylating enzyme remains to be determined.

First, let us survey the pattern of DNA glucosylation by enzymes developed in each of the infections.[18] (Fig. 6). The DNA-glucosylating enzyme found in T2 phage-infected cells transfers a glucosyl group to HMC in α configuration, which is the predominant form of the glucosyl residue attached to the HMC residues in the DNA of T2. After T4 infection, two enzymes were found. One enzyme, like the enzyme pro-

DNA SYNTHESIS IN BACTERIOPHAGE-INFECTED CELLS

Phage	Infected Cell Enzymes
T2, T4, T6	UDP glucose + HMC-DNA → G$\overset{\alpha}{-}$HMC-DNA + UDP
T4	UDP glucose + HMC-DNA → G$\overset{\beta}{-}$HMC-DNA + UDP
T6	UDP glucose + G—HMC-DNA → G$\overset{\beta}{-}$G—HMC-DNA + UDP

Fig. 6. Pattern of DNA-glucosylation by enzymes developed in phage-infected cells.

duced in T2 infection, adds a glucosyl group in α linkage to HMC. The second also adds a glucosyl group to the HMC, but the configuration in this case is β. The enzymatic results are thus compatible with the known composition of T4 DNA, in which all the HMC residues have an α- or β-glucosyl substituent. Two glucosylating enzymes were also found after T6 infection. One of these, like the enzyme of T2 infection, adds an α-monoglucosyl group to HMC. The second reacts with DNA samples containing monoglucosyl-HMC groups but not with unglucosylated HMC groups. Diglucosylated residues are produced in which the linkage between the glucose residues has the β configuration. Here again the results are compatible with the composition of T6 DNA. In no case does an enzyme induced by a given phage add glucose to the DNA of that phage.

The three enzymes that produce α-linked, monoglucosyl groups—one each from the T2, T4, and T6 infection—are referred to as α-glucosyl transferases. The enzyme of T4 infection that produces β-linked monoglucosyl residues are termed T4-β-glucosyl transferase. The enzyme from T6-infected cells that converts mono- to diglucosyl residues is called the T6-β-glucosyl transferase.

As we shall show, these five transferases are distinguishable as different enzymes, although the three α-glucosyl transferases (T2, T4, and T6) are highly similar in most of their functional properties; the two β-glucosyl transferases (T4 and T6) are readily separated from the α-glucosyl transferases by their distinctive properties and are, of course, characterized by their respective transferase functions. It may be simplest to present what we know about this family of transferases in the context of the individual infections.

Glucosylation in T2 Infection. The T2-α-glucosyl transferase purified about 600-fold in relation to the original infected cell extract [19] catalyzes the reaction:

UDP-glucose + HMC-DNA $\rightleftharpoons$

UDP + α-glucosyl-HMC-DNA

The glucosyl groups have been identified in the product as attached exclusively to the HMC residues, in α-configuration (Table 1, line 1) and as monosaccharides.

With either UDP glucose or HMC-DNA present in excess, the reaction goes to completion; the K_m values are $4 \times 10^{-5} M$ UDP glucose and $5 \times 10^{-6} M$ HMC residues (in DNA).

The extent of glucosylation of a synthetic HMC-DNA is in the vicinity of 60% of the HMC residues (Fig. 7) and is not significantly altered when primers of widely varying G-C content are used for synthesis of the HMC-DNA (Table 2, see legend).

Reversal of the reaction can be demonstrated when a high concentration of UDP is provided; UDP is specific among

TABLE 1

Configuration of Glucosyl Linkages in Enzymatically Glucosylated DNA

Transferase	Acceptor	Total Radioactivity in Digest	Radioactivity Released by	
			α-Glucosidase	β-Glucosidase
		cpm×10^{-3}	cpm×10^{-3}	
T2-HMC-α-glucosyl	HMC-DNA	12.6	10.6	0.25
T4-HMC-α-glucosyl	HMC-DNA	17.2	10.9	0.14
T6-HMC-α-glucosyl	HMC-DNA	12.2	10.9	0.22
T4-HMC-β-glucosyl	HMC-DNA	16.8	0.26	14.9
T4-HMC-β-glucosyl	T2 DNA	10.5	0.12	10.1
T6-glucosyl-HMC-β-glucosyl	T4 DNA		0.0	3.3

The C^{14}-glucosylated products were heated for five minutes at 75°, dialyzed against $0.2M$ NaCl, and then digested to nucleosides. Separate aliquots of each digest were treated with α- or β-glucosidase, followed by Norit. The amount of C^{14} that was not adsorbed by Norit (and therefore not bound to nucleotide) was a measure of the glucose released by each glucosidase.

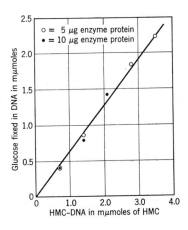

Fig. 7. Limit of glucose fixation in DNA as a function of the amount of DNA added. The HMC-DNA was prepared with thymus DNA as primer.

TABLE 2

Extents of Glucosylation of DNA Acceptors by Glucosyl Transferases

Trans-ferases	Acceptor DNA			
	Synthetic HMC-DNA	T2	T4	T6
	% of total HMC residues glucosylated			
T2-α	50–58	<1	<1	<1
T4-α	66–75	28	<1	<1
T6-α	50–71	28	<1	<1
T4-β	70–78	28	<1	25
T6-β	<1	70	70	<1

The values show the limits of C^{14}-glucose transfer reached under conditions of excess enzyme and UDP-glucose concentrations and extended time of incubation. The values are expressed as a percentage of the calculated total numer of HMC residues in the acceptor DNA added to the reaction mixture. Synthetic HMC-DNA's were enzymatically prepared with primer DNA's from T2, T4, T6, *E. coli*, and calf thymus and tested with all the glucosylating enzymes except the last enzyme; only T2-primed DNA was used with the T6-β-glucosyl transferase. P^{32}-labeled dHMCTP was used in the HMC-DNA synthesis for ease of measuring the amount of HMC in the DNA's. When the P^{32} had decayed and its count was no longer measurable, the glucosylation experiments were carried out. The number of HMC residues in the phage DNA's was calculated as 0.16 mole of HMC per mole of phosphorus.

a variety of nucleotides in accepting glucose from the glucosylated HMC-DNA. The sluggishness of deglucosylation has thwarted our attempts to establish the equilibrium point of the reaction. Limiting values for the extent of the forward and reverse reactions indicates that the equilibrium strongly favors the production of glucosylated HMC residues

$$K = \frac{(\text{glucosyl-HMC})(\text{UDP})}{(\text{HMC})(\text{UDP-glucose})} = 200 - 2000.$$

The maximal extent of glucosylation is apparently not limited by equilibrium considerations, since, as we know, 25% of the HMC residues in T2 DNA are unglucosylated and will accept no glucose in the presence of the T2-α-glucosyl transferase.

Thus the T2-α-glucosyl transferase glucosylates HMC-containing DNA to an extent that approximates that found in T2 DNA and fails to act on T2 DNA itself even though 25% of its HMC residues are free and apparently available for glucosylation. Is the selection by the enzyme of 60% of the HMC residues dictated by the sequences in which these residues are found? The enzyme glucosylates HMC-DNA acceptors of widely different G-C content, suggesting that nucleotide sequence is not a decisive influence. Studies with other transferases show that the secondary structure of the DNA has a profound effect on both the rate and extent of glucosylation. A question that has not been answered is how the diglucosyl groups in T2 DNA are produced. We imagine that an enzyme like the T6-β-glucosyl transferase (see below) is responsible but have not yet succeeded in finding it.

Glucosylation in T4 Infection. Fractionation of the α-glucosyl transferase and the degree of its purification from extracts of T4-infected cells is exactly like that found for the T2-α-glucosyl transferase.[20] It is readily separated by ion-exchange chromatography (Fig. 8) from the T4-β-glucosyl transferase which has been purified about 500-fold.[20]

The T4-α-glucosyl transferase shares the properties and carries out the reaction described for the T2-α-glucosyl trans-

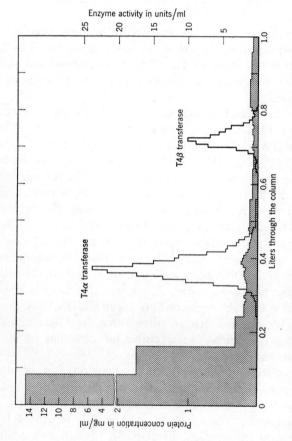

Fig. 8. Chromatographic separation of the T4-α and the T4-β glucosyl transferases on XE-64 resin.

ferase [19, 20] but differs in that it is able to glucosylate T2 DNA; it does not transfer glucose to T4 or T6 DNA (Table 2).

The T4-β-glucosyl transferase catalyzes the reaction

UDP glucose + HMC-DNA $\rightleftharpoons$

UDP + β-glucosyl-HMC-DNA

The β configuration of the glucosyl attachment to the HMC residues (Table 1) and its monosaccharide structure have been established. The K_m values for UDP glucose and HMC-DNA (expressed as HMC residues) were low, as with the α-glucosyl transferases.

With enzyme in excess and/or prolonged incubation periods, the amount of glucose added to a constant amount of DNA approaches a limit (Table 3, Fig. 9). In all instances the β-glucosyl transferase adds glucose to all avail-

TABLE 3

Glucosylation of HMC-Containing DNA's by T4-α and T4-β Transferases

	HMC-Containing DNA		T4-α Transferase		T4-β Transferase	
No.	Source	Available HMC Residues	Rate	Extent	Rate	Extent
		mμmole	μmoles/hr/mg	mμmole	μmoles/hr/mg	mμmole
1	T2 DNA	0.56	13	0.55	310	0.56
2	Heat denatured T2 DNA	0.56	0.8	0.25	47	0.58
3	T4 DNA	0	<0.01	<0.001	<0.01	<0.001
4	T6 DNA	0.49	<0.01	<0.001	127	0.48
5	Synthetic HMC-DNA	1.63	191	0.84	206	1.61

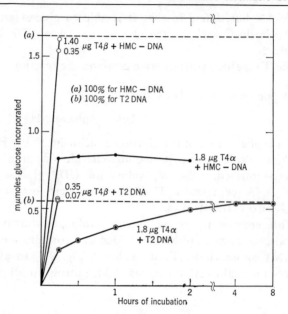

Fig. 9. Extents of glucosylation of HMC-containing DNA's by T4-α-and T4-β-glucosyl transferases. Addition of glucose to a constant amount of DNA (9.1 mμmoles of synthetic HMC-DNA containing 1.63 mμmoles of HMC or 12.5 mμmoles of T2 DNA containing 0.56 mμmole of unglucosylated HMC) was measured in the respective assay mixtures. Increasing amounts of enzyme and prolonged incubation times were employed to determine the maximum glucosylation.

able HMC residues in the acceptor DNA; the α-glucosyl transferase is in general more restricted in extent of glucosylation. Noteworthy is the failure of the α-glucosyl transferase to transfer glucose to T6 DNA; as expected, T4 DNA does not serve as an acceptor for either transferase.

As with the α-glucosyl transferases, reversal of the reaction requires UDP (Table 4). We used the reversibility of the reaction to study the specificity of the α- and β-glucosyl transferases.

We found that glucosyl-HMC-DNA synthesized by the α-glucosyl transferase (and thus possessing α-glucosyl linkages) could be cleaved only by the α-glucosyl transferase (Table 4). Similarly glucosyl-HMC-DNA, synthesized by the β-glucosyl transferase, reacted only with the β-glucosyl transferase in the reverse reaction. In both cases the product of the reverse reaction was identified as UDP glucose. The strict specificity of the transferases with respect to the configuration of the glucosyl attachment is thus manifest in both its attachment to and removal from the HMC residues of DNA. In UDP glucose the glucosyl linkage is α, and it may be inferred therefore that the mechanisms of transfer by the α- and β-glucosyl transferases must differ.

When T4 DNA is acted upon by one or the other of the transferases, we may assume that as in the case of glucosy-

TABLE 4

Reversal of the Reaction

Experiment	Transferase	Glucosyl DNA	UDP	UDP-Glucose
			μmole	mμmole
1	T4-α	HMC—$^{\alpha}$Glucose	0.0	<.001
	T4-α	HMC—$^{\alpha}$Glucose	0.2	.076
	T4-α	HMC—$^{\beta}$Glucose	0.2	<.001
2	T4-β	HMC—$^{\beta}$Glucose	0.0	<.001
	T4-β	HMC—$^{\beta}$Glucose	0.2	.091
	T4-β	HMC—$^{\alpha}$Glucose	0.2	<.001

lated synthetic HMC-DNA the α-glucosyl transferase will remove only α-glucosyl groups and the β-glucosyl transferase only β-glucosyl residues. When these two kinds of specifically "deglucosylated" T4 DNA's were tested as glucosyl acceptors, we found that each DNA would accept glucose transferred by either enzyme (Table 5). Whereas there was a rigid specificity of the enzymes for the configuration of glucosyl linkage, we observed in this experiment α glucosylation of HMC residues that had been attached to glucose by β linkages and β glucosylation of HMC residues that were formerly α-glucosyl.

The presence of the α- and β-glucosyl transferases in T4-infected cells would appear to account for the α- and β-glucosyl linkages in T4 DNA, but the controls that regulate the 70:30 ratio of $\alpha:\beta$ linkages in this DNA are un-

TABLE 5

Addition of Glucose to "Deglucosylated" T4 DNA

Transferase Used to Remove Glucose	Transferase Used to Restore Glucose	Extent of Addition
		mμmole
None	T4-α	<0.001
	T4-β	<0.001
T4-α	T4-α	0.024
	T4-β	0.024
T4-β	T4-α	0.021
	T4-β	0.040

known. For one thing, the T4-β-glucosyl transferase has the capacity to glucosylate all the available HMC groups in an acceptor DNA. For another, our studies suggest that the specificity of the two transferases is not governed by the sequence of bases in the chain. T4 DNA from which some β-glucosyl residues have been removed enzymatically is then capable of accepting α-glucosyl groups in their place; analogously, the T4-β-glucosyl transferase can glucosylate HMC groups which had contained α-glucosyl residues removed by α-glucosyl transferase. It is therefore difficult to explain why in T4 DNA the proportions of β-glucosyl residues is strictly fixed at 30%.

We have found that the α- and β-glucosyl transferase activities in cell-free extracts appear at the same time during the infection cycle.[18] If during phage synthesis the action of one glucosyl transferase preceded the action of the other, the reactions would have to occur in different cell "compartments." An alternative presently more attractive is that the specificity for accepting glucosyl residues may be governed by the secondary or even tertiary structure of the DNA. The secondary structure of the acceptor HMC-DNA has definitely been shown to influence the activity of these enzymes. Heat-denatured HMC-DNA is glucosylated at reduced *rates* by all the enzymes tested and to a lesser *extent* by the α-glucosyl transferases. In the case of bacteriophage DNA's tertiary structure may be especially important as evidenced by the compacting of the DNA before its envelopment by the phage protein coat.[21] A particular folding of the DNA must be required to enable it to fit within the limited dimensions of the phage head. If glucosylation of the DNA occurs when the helix is already folded, the approach of a given glucosylating enzyme might be limited to specific sites, and 70% of the sites might be sterically accessible to the α-glucosyl transferase, 30% to the β.

TABLE 6
Comparison of the Various Glucosyl Transferases

Property	Transferase				
	T2-α	T4-α	T6-α	T4-β	T6-β
Requirement for sulfhydryl	+	+	+	0	+
Effect of Mg^{2+}	0	0	0	+	+
K_m: DNA	$3 \times 10^{-5}M$	$2.5 \times 10^{-5}M$	$3 \times 10^{-5}M$	$3.3 \times 10^{-5}M$ *	
K_m: UDP glucose	$3.6 \times 10^{-5}M$	$0.7 \times 10^{-5}M$	$1.5 \times 10^{-5}M$	$2.1 \times 10^{-5}M$ *	
				$0.6 \times 10^{-5}M$ †	
Behavior in phosphate buffer:					
activity at pH 6.5	4.0	4.0	1.0	0.8	
activity at pH 7.0					
Glucosylation of T2 DNA	0	+	+	+	+
Glucosylation of T4 DNA	0	0	0	0	+
Glucosylation of T6 DNA	0	0	0	+	0

* In phosphate buffer.
† In Ammediol buffer.

Glucosylation in T6 Infection. The α-glucosyl transferase in T6-infected cells was purified extensively by procedures essentially the same as those described for the T2- and T4-α-glucosyl transferases and exhibited most of their properties.[19] However, it differed from the T2 enzyme by its ability to glucosylate T2 DNA and from the T4 enzyme in its activity in phosphate buffers (Tables 2, 6).

We referred earlier to the influence of the secondary structure of acceptor DNA on the transferase activity. Most of these studies were carried out with the T6-α-glucosyl transferase acting on T2 DNA.[19] The T2 DNA collapses on heating and the recovery of helical structure, as Marmur

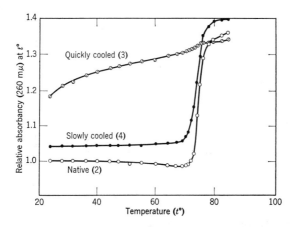

Fig. 10. Thermal transitions of native and of quickly or slowly cooled T2 DNA. The numbers in parentheses indicate the sample preparations. Sample 2 was unheated; sample 3 was heated 15 min at 91° and quickly cooled; sample 4 was like 3 but then reheated and cooled slowly (165 min consumed in going from 91 to 48°). Absorbencies were measured on dialyzed samples after fifteenfold dilution in $0.021M$ Tris buffer, pH 7.5, containing $0.02M$ NaCl.

and Lane [22] and Doty et al.[23] first described, depends on the rate of cooling (Fig. 10). When T2 DNA was denatured by heating and fast cooling the rate of its glucosylation was only 7% of the rate observed with native DNA; the extent of glucosylation was reduced by 60%. The "melting" curve determined by optical measurements and the curve describing the loss of glucosyl acceptor capacity proved quite similar (Fig. 11). When the heat-denatured T2 DNA was reheated and then cooled slowly under renaturing conditions, it showed recovery both of helical structure and of

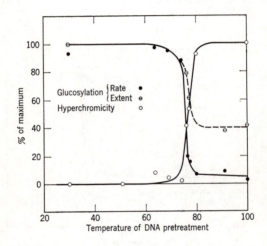

Fig. 11. Activity of T6 transferase on T2 DNA preheated to various temperatures. Aliquots of T2 DNA (1.3 μmoles P per ml in 0.02M Tris buffer, pH 7.5, containing 0.02M NaCl) were heated in sealed tubes for 15 min at the indicated temperatures and quickly cooled in an ice-water bath. The maximal hyperchromicity (measured at 30°) was 28%. The maximal rate of glucosyl transfer with the T6 transferase (0.4 μg of Fraction LV) was 0.60 mμmole per 15 min. The extent of glucosyl transfer shown is the average of three determinations.

glucosyl acceptor functions (threefold increase in rate and 85% of maximal extent).

Like Lehman's diesterase, which may be used to distinguish heat-denatured from native DNA,[24] the glucosyl acceptor function affords an additional criterion for determining intactness of the helical structure of DNA.

The second enzyme identified in extracts of T6-infected cells, T6-β-glucosyl transferase, required DNA with monoglucosyl HMC groups and transferred a glucosyl residue according to the equation

UDP glucose + G-HMC-DNA →

 UDP + G$\overset{\beta}{-}$G-HMC-DNA

T6-β-glucosyl transferase is easily separated from the T6-α-glucosyl transferase but to date has been purified to only a slight extent. Its properties are distinctly different from those of the four transferases so far described (Table 6). Like the α-glucosyl transferases it has sensitive sulfhydryl groups, but like the T4-β-glucosyl transferase it is stimulated by Mg^{2+}.

All HMC-DNA's bearing monoglucosyl groups, except for T6 DNA itself, serve as acceptors; the product was identified as a glucosyl-β-glucosyl disaccharide. Since Kuno and Lehman [17] have characterized the sugar in T6 DNA as a gentiobiosyl (glucosyl-β-1, 6-glucosyl) group in α linkage to HMC, it seems likely that the T6-β-glucosyl transferase produces the same disaccharide.

With T4 DNA as acceptor, a glucosylation limit of 70% of the HMC residues was reached with the T6-β-glucosyl transferase (Table 2), and it might be presumed that the enzyme transferred glucose only to the α-linked glucosyl groups. However, this point has not been checked and no such specificity is apparent from the following experiment with synthetic HMC-DNA. Samples of HMC-DNA were glucosylated with T4-α-glucosyl transferase in one case and T4-β-glucosyl transferase in another. Each of the glucosylated DNA's accepted glucose from the T6-β-glucosyl transferase to a similar extent (Table 2). This lack of specificity does not pose a problem in T6-infected cells, which we assume lack a β-glucosyl transferase that glucosylates HMC groups directly.

We hope that these detailed studies of the purification and properties of phage-induced enzymes will prepare the ground for future work relating DNA structure to the structure and function of specific proteins. Although studies of the transformation of *E. coli* by DNA from the T-series bacteriophages are not advanced, progress along this line is likely. In such studies this phage-host system would be an ideal model for studying correlations between the transforming DNA and proteins whose synthesis is specifically directed. An additional aspect of interest in the particular case of this family of glucosylating enzymes is that DNA is itself a substrate for these enzymes; the factors that control the DNA substrate-enzyme interaction in the glucosylation reaction may have some interesting relationship to the nucleic-acid-protein interaction.

DNA Polymerase. The reason for our initial failure to observe DNA synthesis in extracts of infected cells became clear with the recognition of the phage-induced dCTPase activity. By using fluoride to inhibit the enzyme or by using $d\overline{HMC}TP$ in place of dCTP, we were able to observe polymerase in extracts of infected cells and at levels near those in extracts of uninfected cells.[8] With the addition of heat-denatured DNA as primer, greatly augmented polymerase activities became apparent, and the development of these high levels of polymerase during the course of infection proceeded in the same fashion we and others have already described for other phage-induced enzymes (Fig. 12).

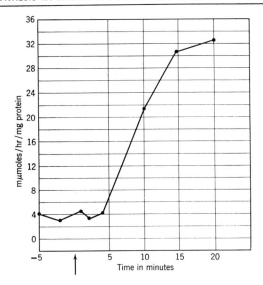

Fig. 12. Polymerase levels after infection assayed with dH̄M̄C̄TP in place of dCTP and with heated DNA as primer.

Do the elevated levels of polymerase after infection represent the same enzyme present in normal cells (which we call *E. coli* polymerase) or is it a new and distinct protein? Several lines of evidence convince us that a new polymerase (which we call T2 polymerase) develops in response to T2 phage infection.[25] The first evidence came from the failure of antiserum directed against *E. coli* polymerase to inhibit the activity in extracts of infected cells. On this basis we assumed the existence of a distinct T2 polymerase and undertook its purification. We found that its physical properties on fractionation differed from those of *E. coli* polymerase; most striking was the disparity in behavior of the two polymerases on a phosphocellulose column (Fig. 13).

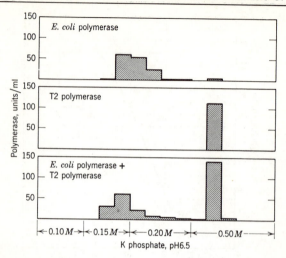

Fig. 13. Chromatography of *E. coli* polymerase and T2 polymerase on phosphocellulose. Primer: heated salmon sperm DNA.

An artificial mixture of the two purified polymerases was readily separated, as predicted from the known migrations of each of the purified enzymes.

With purified T2 polymerase as antigen, we prepared a rabbit antiserum and found that an amount that completely inhibits T2 polymerase shows no inhibition of *E. coli* polymerase (Fig. 14*b*). Similarly, anti-*E. coli*-polymerase serum inhibits the *E. coli* polymerase without affecting T2 polymerase (Fig. 14*a*).

A third point of distinction between the two polymerases is the difference in their sensitivity to the sulfhydryl-binding reagent *p*-chloromercuribenzoate (PCMB). T2 polymerase is inhibited completely at $2 \times 10^{-5} M$ PCMB, whereas the *E. coli* enzyme retains 72% of its activity at this level of PCMB or even at $2 \times 10^{-4} M$.

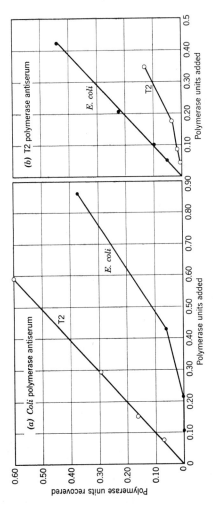

Fig. 14. Selective inhibition of polymerases by specific polymerase antisera. (a) The reaction mixture contained E. coli polymerase antiserum, sodium versenate, NaCl, Tris buffer (7.5), and E. coli polymerase or T2 polymerase. After incubation at 37° for 10 min, the mixture was chilled, an aliquot was removed, and the polymerase activity determined by the standard assay system. (b) The reaction mixture and procedure were as in (a) except that 0.04 ml of T2 polymerase antiserum was used in place of the E. coli polymerase antiserum.

Finally, the two polymerases are distinguishable by their responses to various DNA primers. T2 polymerase is virtually inert with native DNA as primer and seems to react best with collapsed or "single-stranded" molecules. Salmon sperm DNA after heat-denaturation is a rather polydisperse, low-molecular-weight preparation and has proved to be the most active primer for T2 polymerase. Native T2, *E. coli*, or calf thymus DNA samples support only low levels of T2 polymerase activity; after heat denaturation, these DNA preparations are 10 to 30 times more active as primers (Table 7). The T2 and *E. coli* polymerases may be con-

TABLE 7

Relative Effectiveness of Various DNA Primers for T2 Polymerase

Source of DNA	Priming Activity	
	Heated DNA	Native DNA
Salmon sperm	100	5
dGdC	58	—
DNA purified from heated sonicate of T2-infected *E. coli*	57	—
Calf thymus	20	0.7
Salmon liver	15	4
$\phi X174$ bacteriophage	—	13
dAT	11	—
E. coli	10	0.3
T2-bacteriophage	8	0.8

Reaction mixtures contained the standard reagents for polymerase assay with 17 mμmoles of the DNA primer. The value for salmon sperm DNA was set at 100; the other values in the table are expressed on a comparative basis.

trasted by their relative activities with the following DNA's as primers:

DNA	Heated Salmon Sperm	Native Salmon Sperm	Native Calf Thymus	dGdC	dAT
E. coli polymerase	100	200	100	600	1000
T2 polymerase	100	5	1	58	11

The capacity of T2 polymerase to sustain net DNA synthesis is severely limited. With the most highly purified fraction of T2 polymerase and with heated T2 DNA as primer, the amount of DNA synthesized was approximately 14% of the amount of primer added (Fig. 15). (Values as

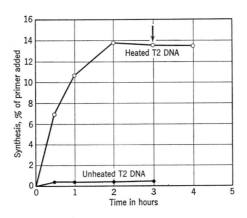

Fig. 15. T2 polymerase activity with native and heat-denatured T2 DNA as primers. The reaction mixture contained Tris buffer (pH 8.6), $MgCl_2$, 2-mercaptoethanol, 150 mμmoles each of dATP, dCTP, dTTP, and dGTP-C^{14}, 300 mμmoles of T2 DNA, and T2 polymerase in a final volume of 0.60 ml. At the time shown by the arrow, more T2 polymerase was added.

high as 75% have been obtained with other preparations of the polymerase.) Unheated T2 DNA was virtually inactive (<0.4%) (Fig. 15). When φX DNA or heated salmon sperm DNA was used as primer, the amount of synthesis was 45 and 60%, respectively. These results are in sharp contrast with the extensive increase (1000 to 2000%) in the DNA enzymatically synthesized with *E. coli* polymerase, using heated or unheated DNA as primer.[20, 24]

The differences just enumerated distinguish the two polymerases as proteins and in certain aspects of their action as well. These differences should not obscure the fact that the basic formulation of *E. coli* polymerase action (see Chapter 1) almost certainly applies equally to T2 polymerase.

Summary and Conclusions

The biochemical changes found in extracts of *E. coli* after infection with the virulent T-even bacteriophages suggest the following series of events. Immediately on entrance of the phage, the *E. coli* genome is immobilized, no longer supporting synthesis of the host proteins nor serving as the template for DNA replication. With the elimination of the *E. coli* genome as a functional entity, the invading phage DNA pre-empts both its phenotypic and genotypic functions.

Recent studies show that within four minutes after infection new enzymic reactions are observed which provide for the synthesis of the distinctive phage DNA (Fig. 16). Certain other reactions present prior to infection are increased in rate by tenfold or greater;[2, 8, 12] these increased reaction rates are assumed to be necessary to support the rapid multiplication of the phage. Presumably the enzymatic machinery of the host cell responsible for energy pro-

DNA SYNTHESIS IN BACTERIOPHAGE-INFECTED CELLS

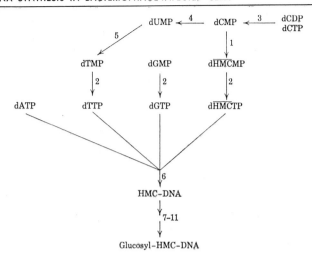

Fig. 16. Enzymes induced by infection with T-even phages for synthesis of phage DNA. 1-Hydroxymethylase,[7] 2-deoxynucleotide kinases,[8–12] 3-dCDPase, dCTPase,[13,14] 4-dCMP deaminase,[26] 5-thymidylate synthetase,[27] 6-polymerase,[25] 7-11-glucosyl transferases.[8,19,20]

duction and various biosyntheses continues to function to support the production of new phages.[10]

Synthesis of *new enzymes,* most probably directed by the invading phage DNA,[7,28] accounts for the novel reactions. Hydroxymethylase converts deoxycytidylate (dCMP) to hydroxymethyldeoxycytidylate (dHMCMP); phosphorylation of dHMCMP to the triphosphate by a new kinase makes it a suitable substrate for polymerization to DNA. The di- and triphosphates of deoxycytidylate are destroyed as possible substrates for DNA synthesis by the action of a new pyrophosphatase, which thereby restores dCMP as a substrate for hydroxymethylation or deamination to deoxyuridylate (precursor of deoxythymidylate). A family of novel glucosyl transferases glucosylate HMC groups in DNA in patterns that characterize each of the different T-even phage DNA's. Increased levels of kinases and polymerase already present in the uninfected cell are actually due to synthesis of new and distinctive enzymes. Thus new enzymes are induced (1) to carry out functions unique to viral DNA synthesis, (2) to neutralize the action of host enzymes antagonistic to viral DNA synthesis, and (3) to supplement the action of host enzymes in order to achieve reaction rates required for rapid viral DNA synthesis. Among the unsolved questions is how the phage pre-empts the functions of the host DNA—how the control of information transfer to protein synthesis and the control of replication are shifted from the host to the phage genome.

REFERENCES

1. Cohen, S. S., *Advances in Virus Research*, **3**, 1 (1955); Hershey, A. D., *ibid.*, **4**, 25 (1957); *Harvey Lectures*, p. 229 (1955–1956); Sinsheimer, R. L., in *The Nucleic Acids* (eds., E. Chargaff and J. N. Davidson), Academic Press, New York, **3**, 187 (1960); Kozloff, L. M., in *A Symposium on Molecular Biology* (ed., R. E. Zirkle), University of Chicago Press, Chicago, p. 178 (1959).
2. Cohen, S. S., *J. Biol. Chem.*, **174**, 281 (1948).
3. Kornberg, A., I. R. Lehman, and E. S. Simms, *Federation Proc.*, **15**, 291 (1956).
4. Wyatt, G. R., and S. S. Cohen, *Biochem. J.*, **55**, 774 (1953).
5. Sinsheimer, R. L., *Science*, **120**, 551 (1954); Volkin, E., *J. Am. Chem. Soc.*, **76**, 5892 (1954); Streisinger, G., and J. Weigle, *Proc. Natl. Acad. Sci. U. S.*, **42**, 504 (1956).
6. Sinsheimer, R. L., *Proc. Natl. Acad. Sci. U. S.*, **42**, 502 (1956); Jesaitis, M. A., *J. Exptl. Med.*, **106**, 233 (1957); *Federation Proc.*, **17**, 250 (1958).
7. Flaks, J. G., and S. S. Cohen, *J. Biol. Chem.*, **234**, 1501 (1959); Flaks, J. G., J. Lichtenstein, and S. S. Cohen, *ibid.*, **234**, 1507 (1959).

8. Kornberg, A., S. B. Zimmerman, S. R. Kornberg, and J. Josse, *Proc. Natl. Acad. Sci. U. S.*, **45,** 772 (1959).
9. Somerville, R., K. Ebisuzaki, and G. R. Greenberg, *Proc. Natl. Acad. Sci. U. S.*, **45,** 1240 (1959).
10. Bessman, M. J., *J. Biol. Chem.*, **234,** 2735 (1959).
11. Bessman, M. J., and M. J. Van Bibber, *Biochem. Biophys. Res. Comm.*, **1,** 101 (1959); L. J. Bello, M. J. Van Bibber, and M. J. Bessman, *J. Biol. Chem.*, **236,** 1467 (1961); *Biochim. et Biophys. Acta,* **53,** 194 (1961).
12. Bessman, M. J., and L. J. Bello, *J. Biol. Chem.*, **236,** PC 72 (1961).
13. Koerner, J. F., M. S. Smith, and J. M. Buchanan, *J. Biol. Chem.*, **235,** 2691 (1960).
14. Zimmerman, S. B., and A. Kornberg, *J. Biol. Chem.*, **236,** 1480 (1961).
15. Maley, F., and S. Ochoa, *J. Biol. Chem.*, **233,** 1538 (1958).
16. Lehman, I. R., and E. A. Pratt, *J. Biol. Chem.*, **235,** 3254 (1960).
17. Kuno, S., and I. R. Lehman, *J. Biol. Chem.*, **237,** 1266 (1962).
18. Kornberg, S. R., S. B. Zimmerman, and A. Kornberg, *J. Biol. Chem.*, **236,** 1487 (1961).
19. Zimmerman, S. B., S. R. Kornberg, and A. Kornberg, *J. Biol. Chem.*, **237,** 512 (1962).
20. Josse, J., and A. Kornberg, *J. Biol. Chem.*, **237,** 1968 (1962).
21. Kellenberger, E., *Advances in Virus Research* (in press).
22. Marmur, J., and D. Lane, *Proc. Natl. Acad. Sci. U. S.*, **46,** 453 (1960).
23. Doty, P., H. Boedtker, J. R. Fresco, R. Haselkorn, and M. Litt, *Proc. Natl. Acad. Sci. U. S.*, **45,** 482 (1959).
24. Lehman, I. R., *J. Biol. Chem.*, **235,** 1479 (1960).
25. Aposhian, H. V., and A. Kornberg, *J. Biol. Chem.*, **237,** 519 (1962).
26. Keck, K., H. R. Mahler, and D. Fraser, *Arch. Biochem. Biophys.*, **86,** 85 (1960).
27. Flaks, J. C., and S. S. Cohen, *J. Biol. Chem.*, **234,** 2981 (1959).
28. Hogness, D., in *The Molecular Control of Cellular Activity* (ed., J. M. Allen), McGraw-Hill, New York, p. 189 (1962).